SRA Imagine It!

Lesson Assessment Book 2

Annotated Teacher's Edition

Level 4

McGraw Hill SRA

A Division of The *McGraw-Hill* Companies

SRAonline.com

 SRA

Send all inquiries to this address:
SRA/McGraw-Hill
4400 Easton Commons
Columbus, OH 43219-6188

ISBN: 978-0-07-613211-9
MHID: 0-07-613211-0

2 3 4 5 6 7 8 9 MAZ 13 12 11 10 09 08

The McGraw-Hill Companies

Table of Contents

Imagine It! Lesson Assessment Books

Lesson Assessment Book 1 and *Lesson Assessment Book 2* are an integral part of a complete assessment program that aligns with the instruction in *Imagine It! Lesson Assessment Book 1* covers material from Units 1–3. *Lesson Assessment Book 2* covers material from Units 4–6. The skills featured in lesson assessments are tied to reading success and reflect both state and national standards.

Lesson Assessment Book 1 and *Lesson Assessment Book 2* offer the opportunity for summative and formative assessment. As students complete each lesson, they will be assessed on their understanding of the instructional content and the literature in each lesson. The results of the assessments will then be used to inform subsequent instruction. How students score on the assessments offers a picture of current student achievement status while also guiding you toward appropriate instructional decisions.

Each lesson assessment offers you the ability to gauge students' understanding of and growth in the following areas:

• Vocabulary
• Comprehension
• Grammar, Usage, and Mechanics
• Oral Fluency
• Writing

Lesson Assessments

The lesson assessments consist of the following:

Lesson Area	Format	Scope	Scoring
Vocabulary	Multiple Choice	Selection Vocabulary and Word Structure elements	10 points (5 questions x 2 point)
Comprehension	Multiple Choice	Comprehension Skills	5 points (5 questions x 1 point)
	Short Answer	Comprehension Skills	10 points (5 questions x 2 points)
	Linking to the Concepts (Short Answer)	General comprehension related to a selection	4 points (0-4 rubrics)
	Personal Response (Short Answer)	General comprehension related to a selection	3 points (0-3 rubrics)
	Analyzing the Selection (Extended Response)	Understanding and development of ideas about selections and the unit theme	8 points (0-8 rubrics)
Grammar, Usage, and Mechanics	Multiple Choice	Grammar, Usage, and Mechanics skills practiced in the lesson	10 points (5 questions x 2 point)
Oral Fluency	Teacher-Directed Student Performance	Oral fluency development from lesson to lesson	Accuracy Rate on 100-point scale

Students will be graded on their understanding of the vocabulary, word structure, comprehension, and grammar, usage, and mechanics skills taught in the lesson on a 50-point scale. A score of 80% (or 40 points out of 50) or higher on each lesson assessment is expected. Students may look back at the selection to answer the assessment questions. Students who consistently fall below 80% should be monitored for possible intervention. Students who are consistent low-performers in one or more aspects of the lesson assessment should be offered more practice in this lesson area during Workshop.

The Oral Fluency Assessments are scored separately. These assessments offer further data on student abilities. Student performance on oral fluency assessments is often a reliable predictor of student growth and understanding in other lesson areas. Students with consistently low accuracy rates and below-level words per minute numbers should be provided extra fluency practice during Workshop.

End of Unit Writing Prompt

Over the course of the year, students will encounter six writing prompts, two each in the narrative, expository, and persuasive genres. These prompts reflect students' prior knowledge and experience with writing to a specific genre. Each prompt consists of a writing situation, a specific audience, directions for writing, and a checklist students can reference to ensure they receive the best score possible. Rubrics for scoring student work follow each prompt in this book. These rubrics pertain to genre, writing traits, and conventions. Students will be graded on a 20-point scale based on the rubrics—four points multiplied by five key writing features.

A score of 75% (or 15 points out of 20) or higher on each writing prompt is expected. Students can respond to the prompts in their student workbooks.

Scores and Records

The opening page of each lesson assessment includes a place for students to write their names and the date, and for you to list their scores.

The Oral Fluency Assessment includes a box in which to write the accuracy rate.

The writing prompt includes a place for students to write their names and the date, and for you to list their scores.

Students' scores in the assessment can be registered in the Oral Fluency Scores, Class Assessment Record, and Student Assessment Record pages.

Lesson Assessment Sections

Students may look back at the selection to answer the assessment questions.

Vocabulary

Each vocabulary assessment is comprised of five multiple-choice questions worth two points each. Four of the questions feature selection vocabulary words from the lesson students have just completed. The remaining question in the assessment pertains to a word structure element from that lesson. The format of this question varies based on the word structure feature that is being assessed.

Comprehension: Multiple Choice

Each comprehension assessment begins with five multiple-choice questions worth one point each. The items reflect the comprehension skills students have been taught specifically in that lesson and skills students have been previously taught.

Comprehension: Short Answer

Next, students answer five short-answer questions worth two points each. These questions also reflect comprehension skills specific to the lesson and to students' prior knowledge and understanding of comprehension skills. Well-crafted and concise responses that answer the question fully should be awarded two points. Answers that partially address the question or are confusing and incomplete should be awarded a point, at your discretion. Answers that do not attempt to address the question or provide incorrect information should receive zero points.

Please note the "Possible answers below" following the directions in this Teacher's Edition. This serves as a reminder that students do not have to provide the exact answer shown, and that in some cases more than one answer is possible. For example, questions that ask for "one reason" or "one example" of something might be answered by a reason or example not specified in this Teacher's Edition.

Comprehension: Linking to the Concepts

In this section, students craft a response to a question related to the selection they have just read. These questions do not focus on a particular comprehension skill; rather, they assess general comprehension of a selection by focusing on a key element in a selection which students should be comfortable identifying and writing to or about. These questions are worth four points each. Use the following criteria to judge student responses. To fully answer the question or prompt, student answers should be approximately forty to sixty words.

Score: 4

The student understands the question and responds using information from the selection. The response is correct, reflects a thorough comprehension of the selection, and is an acceptably complete answer to the question. The organization of the response is meaningful, it is written smoothly, and sentences flow together. The response focuses on the topic. If multiple paragraphs are written, they are linked to one another with effective transitions. The response reads easily and demonstrates a sense of audience. It has correct spelling, grammar, usage, and mechanics, and it is written neatly and legibly.

Score: 3

The student understands the question and responds using information from the selection. The response may reflect comprehension of the selection and is a somewhat complete answer to the question. The organization of the response is meaningful, it is written smoothly, and sentences flow together. The response focuses on the topic. If multiple paragraphs are written, they are linked to one another with effective transitions. The response reads easily and demonstrates a sense of audience. It has occasional errors in spelling, grammar, usage, and mechanics, and it is mostly written neatly and legibly.

Score: 2

The student has partial understanding of the question. The response may reflect limited comprehension of the selection and is an incomplete answer to the question. The organization of the response is weak, it is written carelessly, and sentences are somewhat disorganized. The response includes extraneous information. If multiple paragraphs are written, they are linked to one another ineffectively. The response requires some effort to read easily and demonstrates a poor sense of audience. It has occasional errors in spelling, grammar, usage, and mechanics, and it is written somewhat neatly and legibly.

Score: 1

The student has minimal understanding of the question. The response may reflect poor comprehension of the selection and is a barely acceptable answer to the question. The organization of the response is imprecise, it is written erratically, and sentences may be disjointed. The response is poorly focused. If multiple paragraphs are written, they are linked to one another inconsistently. The response is difficult to follow and may cause the reader to struggle. It has frequent errors in spelling, grammar, usage, and mechanics, and it is written with borderline neatness and legibility.

Score: 0

The student fails to compose a response. If a response is attempted, it is inaccurate, meaningless, or irrelevant. The response may be written so poorly that it is neither legible nor understandable.

SAMPLE

The following is an example of a response that would receive a score of "3" if it were mostly written neatly and legibly. The student shows an understanding of the question and relates information pertaining to the selection. The answer is organized, and the sections of the response relate to one another. However, the response spends more effort than needed describing *what* compost is, and the errors in spelling and grammar prevent it from being an exemplary response.

Linking to the Concepts *Why do some people have compost piles?*

A compost pile uses rot to make good soil. People put garbige and things like leaves or grass in a compost pile. After a while the stuff rots and it turns into a kind of dirt that is good for a garden. These people probably have gardens.

Comprehension: Personal Response

In this section, students are asked to craft a personal response related to an idea or thematic issue raised by the selection they have just read. This section judges students' level of comprehension by assessing their ability to connect what they have just read to a personal level.

These questions are worth three points each. Use the following criteria to judge student responses. To fully answer the question or prompt, student answers should be approximately forty to sixty words.

Score: 3

The student understands the question and responds suitably using a personal experience, opinion, prior knowledge, or plausible conjecture. The response reflects a thorough comprehension of the selection and is an acceptably complete answer to the question. The organization of the response is meaningful, it is written smoothly, and sentences flow together. The response focuses on the topic. If multiple paragraphs are written, they are linked to one another with effective transitions. The response reads easily and demonstrates a sense of audience. It has correct spelling, grammar, usage, and mechanics, and it is written neatly and legibly.

Score: 2

The student understands the question and responds using a personal experience, opinion, prior knowledge, or plausible conjecture. The response may reflect partial comprehension of the selection and is a somewhat complete answer to the question. The organization of the response is imprecise, it is written erratically, and sentences may be somewhat disjointed. The response is not clearly focused. If multiple paragraphs are written, they are linked to one another ineffectively. The response is difficult to follow and demonstrates little awareness of the reader. It has a moderate number of errors in spelling, grammar, usage, and mechanics, and it is mostly written neatly and legibly.

Score: 1

The student has minimal understanding of the question and responds using a personal experience, opinion, prior knowledge, or plausible conjecture. The response may reflect poor comprehension of the selection and is a barely acceptable answer to the question. The organization of the response is imprecise, it is written erratically, and sentences may be disjointed. The response is poorly focused. If multiple paragraphs are written, they are linked to one another inconsistently. The response is difficult to follow and may cause the reader to struggle. It has frequent errors in spelling, grammar, usage, and mechanics, and it is written with borderline neatness and legibility.

Score: 0

The student fails to compose a response. If a response is attempted, it is inaccurate, meaningless, or irrelevant. The response may be written so poorly that it is neither legible nor understandable.

The following is an example of a response that would receive a score of "2" if it were mostly written neatly and legibly. The student shows an understanding of the question and connects it to plausible, real-world situations. However, the response ends abruptly, the student leaves it up to the reader to supply the resolution, and there are errors in spelling and grammar. These facts prevent it from being an exemplary response.

SAMPLE

Personal Response *Write about a mystery you solved. How did you solve it?*

> *There was some mud on a piece of wood in our garage. I didn't know how it got there. Nobody else knew then I saw like a hole in the mud. I remembered in science we learned about waspses, like bees. They make nests for their babies out of mud.*

Grammar, Usage, and Mechanics

Each grammar, usage, and mechanics assessment is comprised of five multiple-choice questions worth two points each. Each question specifically relates to the lesson material for that week. Students sometimes will be asked to identify errors or incorrect constructions, so remind students to read each question carefully.

Comprehension: Analyzing the Selection

This section of the assessment allows students to craft a longer, more detailed response to show their comprehension of what they have read. It also provides additional data on the writing skills of students as they progress through the program.

Students will sometimes be asked to respond by connecting the selection they have just read to previous selections in the unit.

These questions and prompts are worth eight points each. Use the following criteria to judge student responses. To fully answer the question or prompt, student answers should be approximately one hundred to one hundred and fifty words.

Note: You will notice that the rubrics below each have a two-point range. Use your professional judgment in awarding the higher point total in the scale to students' work.

Score: 8 or 7

The student understands the question and responds suitably using the appropriate source of information. These sources include the selection itself, other selections, personal experience, opinion, prior knowledge, or plausible conjecture. The response reflects a thorough comprehension of the selection and is an acceptably complete answer to the question. The organization of the response is meaningful, it is written smoothly, and both sentences and paragraphs flow together. Paragraphs focus on related topics and are linked to one another with effective transitions. The response reads easily and demonstrates a sense of audience. It has correct spelling, grammar, usage, and mechanics, and it is written neatly and legibly.

Score: 6 or 5

The student understands the question and responds suitably using the appropriate source of information. These sources include the selection itself, other selections, personal experience, opinion, prior knowledge, or plausible conjecture. The response may reflect comprehension of the selection or other sources and is a somewhat complete answer to the question. The organization of the response is somewhat meaningful, and both sentences and paragraphs flow together relatively smoothly. Paragraphs focus on related topics and are linked to one another with effective transitions. The response reads easily and demonstrates a sense of audience. It has occasional errors in spelling, grammar, usage, and mechanics, and it is written somewhat neatly and legibly.

Score: 4 or 3

The student has partial understanding of the question. The response may reflect limited comprehension of the selection and is an incomplete answer to the question or includes irrelevant information. The organization of the response is weak, it is written carelessly, and both sentences and paragraphs are somewhat disorganized. Paragraphs include some extraneous information and are linked to one another ineffectively. The response requires some effort to read easily and demonstrates a poor sense of audience. It has occasional errors in spelling, grammar, usage, and mechanics, and it is written somewhat neatly and legibly.

Score: 2 or 1

The student has minimal understanding of the question. The response may reflect poor comprehension of the selection and is a barely acceptable answer to the question or includes irrelevant information. The organization of the response is imprecise, it is written erratically, and sentences or paragraphs may be disjointed. Paragraphs may be poorly focused or are linked to one another inconsistently. The response is difficult to follow and may cause the reader to struggle. It has frequent errors in spelling, grammar, usage, and mechanics, and it is written with borderline neatness and legibility.

Score: 0

The student fails to compose a response. If a response is attempted, it is inaccurate, meaningless, or irrelevant. The response may be written so poorly that it is neither legible nor understandable.

The following is an example of a response that would receive a score of "5" if written somewhat neatly and legibly. The student shows an understanding of the question in the opening paragraphs. The student makes few errors in spelling and grammar. However, after the opening paragraphs the focus drifts, and no mention of bridge technology is made. These facts prevent it from being an exemplary response.

SAMPLE

Analyzing the Selection *How are the Golden Gate Bridge and the completion of the transcontinental railroad alike? Write about the people involved, the technology they used, and what was accomplished.*

The Golden Gate Bridge and the transcontinental railroad are alike because they joined things. The bridge joined land on both sides of San Francisco bay. It made it easier to cross the bay. The railroad joined the United States east to west.

A lot of people worked on both things. They must have worked hard and they took a long time. I think the bridge must have been more dangerous. People could fall off the bridge.

One way they were different is how they was built. The railroad had been around for a while. They put down the rails in the same way they always had with wood under the metal rails and spikes holding the rails down. It was probably hard coming over mountains because they had to make tunnels through mountains. The deserts were probably hard too.

The bridge must have been really hard to make because of the deep water. It must have been scarey. I don't know how people thought of how to make the bridge.

Oral Fluency Assessments

Administering Oral Fluency Assessments

The Oral Fluency Assessment is an efficient means for evaluating students' ability to read. It is simple to administer and score, yet it provides extraordinarily useful quantitative and qualitative data. You will find oral fluency assessments for each lesson. The words in the selections are of sufficient variety to allow for an analysis of the decoding and vocabulary abilities of a student and to draw inferences about a student's ability to derive meaning from the text.

Make a copy of the Oral Fluency Assessment for each student you will be assessing. Have students turn to the corresponding page in their workbooks. Be sure you have a pen or pencil, a stopwatch or other timer, and extra paper to record any observations. Briefly review the text before you begin. On the Oral Fluency Scores pages, you will record the student's name, the date of the assessment, and the results of the assessment.

Have the student sit comfortably at a table with you. Seat yourself and the student so that you can mark the assessment unobtrusively without distracting the student.

Say: *Here is a selection I would like you to read aloud for me. I am going to listen to you read and take some notes. The notes I take will help me learn how well you can read. You will not be graded for this, so you should not feel nervous. Read the selection carefully and do your best. Take a few minutes now to look over the selection, and then I will tell you when to begin.*

Allow time for the student to preview the story. Be sure you have a pen or pencil.

Say: *Are you ready?* (Check to be sure the student is ready.) *You may begin now.*

Start the timer or watch as the student begins to read. You may pronounce any proper nouns with which the student is unfamiliar. Do not count these words as errors.

Note: If the student becomes frustrated or makes several consecutive errors, stop the assessment.

At the end of one minute place a bracket ( ]) at the end of the last word the student reads.

Scoring Oral Fluency Assessments

The following guidelines will help you score the assessment accurately and consistently.

- Self-correcting should not be counted as an error.
- Repeating the same mistake should be counted as only one error.
- Hesitating for more than five seconds—at which point you would have provided the word—should count as an error.
- Become familiar with the evaluating codes before administering the Oral Fluency Assessment.

Scoring Conventions

- Draw a line through any word that is misread. Count this as an error. If possible, note the type of error. (Misreading *short a* as *short e*, reading *get* as *jet*, and so on).
- Draw a bracket ( ]) at the end of the last word the student reads in one minute.
- Words the student omits should be counted as errors, even if you prompt the student.
- Indicate with a caret extra words that have been inserted. If possible, write the inserted word. Count insertions as errors.
- Draw an arrow between words that have been reversed. Count these as one error.
- Students might repeat words on occasion. Do not count this behavior as an error.

Finding the Student's Accuracy Rate

To find a student's accuracy rate, count the total number of words read in one minute. The numbers beside the passage on the teacher's page will make this an easier task. Subtract the number of errors from the total number of words read and use that figure to find the number of correct words read per minute. Then divide the correct words per minute by the total number of words read to find the accuracy rate. Record these numbers on the Reading Rate and Accuracy chart located on your Oral Fluency Assessment pages.

- Record the student's score on the Oral Fluency Scores pages and the Student Assessment Record.
- Complete the Reading Fluency scale at the bottom of your Oral Fluency Assessment page. These qualitative measures indicate your subjective judgment of how the student compares with other students who are reading at grade level.

READING RATE AND ACCURACY

Total Words Read:	130
Number of Errors:	19
Number of Correct Words Read Per Minute (WPM):	111
Accuracy Rate:	85%

(Number of Correct Words Read per Minute ÷ Total Words Read)

READING FLUENCY

	Low	Average	High
Decoding ability	○	○	●
Pace	○	●	○
Syntax	○	●	○
Self-correction	○	●	○
Intonation	○	○	●

Interpreting the Oral Fluency Assessments

First, compare the student's number of correct words per minute with the following chart. This will give you an idea of how the student compares with other students in the same grade at the same time of year. The data in this chart represents the approximate number of correct words read per minute a student should be reading in Grades 2–6. The two rows of numbers represent the 50th and 75th percentiles.

	Units 1-2	Units 3-4	Units 5-6	
Grade 2	79	100	117	75th Percentile
	51	72	89	50th Percentile
Grade 3	99	120	137	75th Percentile
	71	92	107	50th Percentile
Grade 4	119	139	152	75th Percentile
	94	112	123	50th Percentile
Grade 5	139	156	168	75th Percentile
	110	127	139	50th Percentile
Grade 6	153	167	177	75th Percentile
	127	140	150	50th Percentile

Source Adapted from Hasbrouck, J., & Tindal, G. (2005). Oral Reading Fluency: 90 Years of Measurement (Tech. Rep. No. 33). Eugene, Oregon: University of Oregon, College of Education, Behavioral Research and Teaching.

Then examine the student's accuracy rate. Reading accuracy should remain constant or gradually increase within a grade and between grades, until it stabilizes at ninety percent or higher. You may find it helpful to compare a student's accuracy rate after each administration to ensure that it remains constant or increases.

Next, examine the types of errors the student is making and consider how they represent underlying student behaviors. Here are some examples:

- Inserting extra words suggests that the student understands what is read, is constructing meaning, but is reading somewhat impulsively.

- A student who refuses to attempt to read a word is probably uncertain of his or her abilities and is unwilling to take risks.

- Misreading regular letter sounds implies that the student has not yet mastered the conventions of the sound-symbol relationship. This is in contrast with the student who misreads complex letter sounds (alternate sounds, blends, diphthongs, digraphs, and so on) but has little difficulty with regular letter sounds.

Finally, consider the error pattern. If errors are scattered randomly throughout the passage, then the error types represent skills the student has not yet developed. If errors increase in frequency from beginning to end, then fatigue or inattention likely are involved.

Other Considerations

Several strategies are available for promoting reading fluency and accuracy. These involve pairing an accomplished reader with a developing reader, small-group choral reading, and repeated readings of familiar text.

You may find it useful to establish targets for reading accuracy. These targets may include goals such as reading ten words in a row without error, increasing by increments the number of correct words a student reads in a minute, or decreasing a specific error type. Establishing such targets allows you to provide appropriate instructional support and gives students a reasonable goal.

End of Unit Writing Prompt

The writing prompt offers the opportunity for an on-demand writing performance similar to the type students will encounter in high-stakes testing. Use the rubrics that follow the prompts to judge students' work. Student writing should be included in each student's Writing Portfolio.

Teacher Records

This Teacher's Edition contains record keeping material that will help you keep track of student progress in lesson assessments.

Six Point Rubrics

Six Point Writing Rubrics for assessing student writing are included.

These can take the place of the four point rubrics if you are in a school that uses the six point rubric system.

Oral Fluency Scores

These pages allow you to note student accuracy rates throughout the year.

Class Assessment Record

These pages offer a warehouse for class scores.

The spaces following the student's name allow for the recording of student scores in each lesson assessment (out of the 50-point scale) and each writing prompt (using the four point or six point rubrics to assess).

The format of the Class Assessment Record provides an easy way to monitor student growth across the year.

Student Assessment Record

You can duplicate this page for each student and use it to track student progress.

Comprehension Observation Log

Observing students as they read anthology selections is an effective way to learn their strengths and areas of need in comprehension. Use the Comprehension Observation Log to record your observations of students. Choose a small set of students to focus on for a particular lesson. You might want to observe students more than once to get a clear idea of their comprehension of texts. Copy this page for each student or group of students you observe.

Name _____ Date _____ Score _____

The Scientific Method

Vocabulary

Read each item. Fill in the bubble for the answer you think is correct.

1. Which suffix means "having to do with"?

Ⓐ -or

Ⓒ -ous

Ⓑ -est

Ⓓ -ic

2. Another word for **certain** is

Ⓐ sure.

Ⓒ elsewhere.

Ⓑ clear.

Ⓓ lower.

3. The chickens seem **crabbier** than when you left. This means that the chickens are

Ⓐ much more active.

Ⓑ in a worse mood.

Ⓒ less vocal.

Ⓓ more eager to fly.

4. We **examine** an experiment in this selection. **Examine** means about the same as

Ⓐ do not understand.

Ⓑ look closely at.

Ⓒ act differently because of the results.

Ⓓ remember well.

5. The farmer might not be **anxious** to share his secret. In this sentence, **anxious** means

Ⓐ nervous.

Ⓒ eager.

Ⓑ forced.

Ⓓ afraid.

The Scientific Method (continued)

Comprehension

Read the following questions carefully. Then completely fill in the bubble of each correct answer. You may look back at the selection to find the answer to each of the questions.

1. Each of these was a reason for taking a one-month vacation from the chicken farm EXCEPT

   Ⓐ the clucking was bothering you.

   Ⓑ the feathers made you sneeze.

   Ⓒ you were allergic to eggs.

   Ⓓ you got tired of chickens.

2. Why did the author write this selection?

   Ⓐ to show the steps involved in designing a good experiment

   Ⓑ to convince people to raise chickens as a hobby

   Ⓒ to tell a funny story about chickens

   Ⓓ to explain why it is important to give animals the right food

The Scientific Method (continued)

3. Which of these is a fact mentioned in the selection?

Ⓐ The chickens liked the Acme Deluxe Chicken Feed better.

Ⓑ The chickens are crabbier since you left.

Ⓒ The other farmer takes better care of your chickens than you do.

Ⓓ Your chickens laid eggs while you were gone.

4. What happens right after your vacation?

Ⓐ You check your records.

Ⓑ You write a paper.

Ⓒ You give your chickens more water.

Ⓓ You form a hypothesis.

5. What is a hypothesis?

Ⓐ a science experiment

Ⓑ a type of guess

Ⓒ a type of chicken feed

Ⓓ a conclusion

The Scientific Method (continued)

Read the following questions carefully. Use complete sentences to answer the questions. Possible answers below

6. What was different about the chicken farm while you were on vacation?

A farmer took care of the chickens; he gave them more water and a different feed.

7. What is the next step after you form a hypothesis?

You need to test your hypothesis.

8. Why are you designing this experiment?

You want to know why your chickens laid more eggs while you were gone.

9. Think about the experiment you do after you have decided that the amount of water did not make a difference. What is the difference between the control and the experimental group of chickens?

The experimental group gets Acme Deluxe Chicken Feed, and the control group gets the regular feed.

10. What are the two steps in the scientific method that occur before forming a hypothesis?

The two steps are asking a question and gathering information.

The Scientific Method (continued)

Read the question below. Write complete sentences for your answer. Support your answer with information from the selection.

Linking to the Concepts Why do scientists conduct experiments?

_____

_____

_____

_____

_____

Read the question below. Your answer should be based on your own experience. Write complete sentences for your answer.

Personal Response What did you learn from this selection about experiments?

_____

_____

_____

_____

_____

_____

The Scientific Method (continued)

Grammar, Usage, and Mechanics

Read each question. Fill in the bubble beside the answer in each group that is correct. If none of the answers is correct, choose the last answer, "none of the above."

1. In which sentence is the verb in the present tense?

Ⓐ The car rolled.　　　Ⓒ Settlers went West.

Ⓑ Pam likes it.　　　Ⓓ none of the above

2. In which sentence is the verb in the past tense?

Ⓐ Two of my friends played on the porch.

Ⓑ The cat curls up on the porch in the sun.

Ⓒ The sun shines overhead at noon.

Ⓓ none of the above

3. In which sentence is the verb in the past tense?

Ⓐ Kip throws the ball to his dog Jasper.

Ⓑ Amy forgot her running shoes again.

Ⓒ We usually meet at the park after school.

Ⓓ none of the above

4. In which sentence is the verb correct?

Ⓐ Dad and Pedro is in the railway station.

Ⓑ The newspaper are still in the driveway.

Ⓒ Mom and I am soon leaving on our vacation.

Ⓓ none of the above

5. In which sentence is the verb incorrect?

Ⓐ An owl was outside my window last night.

Ⓑ Ten people were in the elevator yesterday morning.

Ⓒ Ms. Brennan and Mom seed a movie.

Ⓓ none of the above

The Scientific Method (continued)

Analyzing the Selection

Read the questions below. Write complete sentences for your answer. Support your answer with information from the selection.

Think about an experiment you would like to perform. What is the experiment, and why you would like to perform it? Explain what the experimental and control groups would be.

_____

_____

_____

_____

_____

_____

_____

_____

_____

_____

_____

_____

The Scientific Method (continued)

Oral Fluency Assessment

Clouds

Our Earth is often covered by clouds. If we could look down from a spaceship, we would see bands of gray streaks and mounds that look like fluffy cotton. Some might seem like thin strips of spider webs.

The clouds that usually bring rain are called nimbus clouds. They are large and dark. They often rise up high in the sky. Wispy, light clouds that appear very high in the sky are called cirrus clouds. They appear when the weather is about to be stormy.

Cumulus clouds are large, white, and puffy. They look very much like cotton balls. They appear on fair days. Sometimes cumulus clouds form thunderheads on hot, moist days.

Clouds are made up of water vapor. They form when water on Earth evaporates and changes to a gas in the air. This water comes from lakes, rivers, and oceans. When the water vapor rises to where it cools, it mixes with tiny pieces of dust to form clouds. Cooler air cannot hold as much water as warm air, so the water falls back to the ground in the form of rain.

	1–12
	13–23
	24–34
	35–38
	39–48
	49–61
	62–73
	74–83
	84–85
	86–95
	96–105
	106–113
	114–124
	125–137
	138–147
	148–161
	162–173
	174–185

EVALUATING CODES FOR ORAL FLUENCY

sky   (/) words read incorrectly

blue
^   sky   (^) inserted word
           ( ]) after the last word

READING RATE AND ACCURACY

Total Words Read: _____

Number of Errors: _____

Number of Correct Words
Read Per Minute (WPM):   _____

Accuracy Rate: _____

(Number of Correct Words Read per Minute ÷ Total Words Read)

READING FLUENCY

	Low	Average	High
Decoding ability	○	○	○
Pace	○	○	○
Syntax	○	○	○
Self-correction	○	○	○
Intonation	○	○	○

Record student rates on the Oral Fluency Scores pages.

Name _____ Date _____ Score _____

Magnetism

Vocabulary

Read each item. Fill in the bubble for the answer you think is correct.

1. Rarely means about the same as

(A) lightly.　　　(C) surely.

(B) not often.　　(D) not cooked.

2. *Un-* and *dis-* are examples of

(A) time prefixes.　　(C) number prefixes.

(B) location prefixes.　(D) negative prefixes.

3. The Earth has a hot iron **core.** The **core** of something is its

(A) central part.

(B) top.

(C) warmest part.

(D) length.

4. An electric **current** can produce its own magnetic field. In this sentence, a **current** is a

(A) flow.

(B) tide.

(C) very thin wire.

(D) unit of measurement.

5. There is no **friction** from wheels on rails on a magnetic train. **Friction** is

(A) rolling.

(B) a loud noise.

(C) rubbing.

(D) a force which uses no energy.

Magnetism (continued)

Comprehension

Read the following questions carefully. Then completely fill in the bubble of each correct answer. You may look back at the selection to find the answer to each of the questions.

1. What are most magnets made of?

Ⓐ plastic or rubber

Ⓑ iron or steel

Ⓒ air and water

Ⓓ dirt and water

2. What is the push or pull of a magnet called?

Ⓐ magnetic reaction

Ⓑ magnetic electricity

Ⓒ magnetic force

Ⓓ magnetic generation

Magnetism (continued)

3. What makes a compass work?

Ⓐ electricity from the air

Ⓑ the gravitational pull of the moon

Ⓒ the tides

Ⓓ Earth's magnetic force

4. Which of these has an electromagnet in it?

Ⓐ a doorbell

Ⓑ a dinner plate

Ⓒ a sofa

Ⓓ a paperclip

5. A North pole of a magnet will always be attracted to

Ⓐ the North pole of another magnet.

Ⓑ plastic.

Ⓒ the South pole of another magnet.

Ⓓ a compass.

Magnetism (continued)

Read the following questions carefully. Use complete sentences to answer the questions. Possible answers below

6. In what form is iron usually found?

It is rarely found in its pure form. It is usually mixed with other metals.

7. Why are magnets sometimes labeled at their poles?

They are labeled so that the poles that attract each other are identified.

8. In the first project, why do you test the nail first to see if it is magnetic?

You need to know that it is the experiment that makes it magnetic.

9. How does the Earth act like a huge bar magnet?

Earth has a north and a south magnetic pole.

10. Why is a magnetic train faster than an ordinary train?

It "floats" above its track and has less friction than an ordinary train.

Magnetism (continued)

Read the question below. Write complete sentences for your answer. Support your answer with information from the selection.

Linking to the Concepts How are electricity and magnetism related?

_____

_____

_____

_____

Read the prompt below. Your response should be based on your own experience. Write complete sentences for your response.

Personal Response Write about some of the things you use that contain magnets or electromagnets. Explain how the magnets help those things work.

_____

_____

_____

_____

Magnetism (continued)

Grammar, Usage, and Mechanics

Read each question. Fill in the bubble beside the answer in each group that is correct. If none of the answers is correct, choose the last answer, "none of the above."

1. In which sentence is the verb in the present tense?

   Ⓐ Only the emperor wore a yellow robe.

   Ⓑ The new rug made the room brighter.

   Ⓒ Waves crash over the sides of the boat.

   Ⓓ none of the above

2. In which sentence is the verb in the past tense?

   Ⓐ My younger sister liked the bears at the zoo.

   Ⓑ The lizard sits in the sun getting warm.

   Ⓒ That mechanic works on boat motors.

   Ⓓ none of the above

3. In which sentence is the verb in the past tense?

   Ⓐ Grandma wound up the ball of yarn.

   Ⓑ People stand in line for hours to see popular movies.

   Ⓒ Customers pay for lunch over there.

   Ⓓ none of the above

4. In which sentence is the verb correct?

   Ⓐ You am not going.   Ⓒ Are I in the right room?

   Ⓑ It is important.   Ⓓ none of the above

5. In which sentence is the verb incorrect?

   Ⓐ Armando and Dylan were the first ones finished.

   Ⓑ The calf was born last spring.

   Ⓒ Two people thought he was right.

   Ⓓ none of the above

Magnetism (continued)

Analyzing the Selection

Read the question below. Write complete sentences for your answer. Support your answer with information from the selection.

Suppose you invented a super-powerful magnet. What are some things you might make with it? Use your imagination. Think about everyday problems you might solve as well as new inventions.

_____

_____

_____

_____

_____

_____

_____

_____

_____

_____

_____

_____

Magnetism (continued)

Oral Fluency Assessment

At Grandmother's House

Fran's mother put her arms around Fran and brushed back her long, dark hair. Fran's mother had been sick and needed lots of rest this summer. Grandmother would take good care of Fran, and she would come home at the end of summer. Everything would be better then.

On the day she arrived at Grandmother's house, Fran tried to find something wrong, but she could not. Her home had flowers, trees, and a white fence. Grandmother baked bread and cooked the same type of food that Fran's mother made. Grandmother smiled and told her, "I'm so glad you've come, Fran."

Grandmother showed Fran her pet bird, Flo, and the dog, Carl. Flo chirped at her, and Carl brought his ball for Fran to throw.

That afternoon, Fran saw some children next door. She asked Grandmother about them. Grandmother said, "Oh, that's Sally and her brother Sid. They are twins, and they are the same age as you. I know you'll get along and play together."

Fran smiled. She would miss her family and friends back home, but this might be a good summer after all.

1–10	
11–21	
22–31	
32–43	
44–48	
49–57	
58–68	
69–77	
78–88	
89–98	
99–100	
101–110	
111–122	
123–124	
125–133	
134–141	
142–153	
154–165	
166–175	
176–185	

EVALUATING CODES FOR ORAL FLUENCY

sky (/) words read incorrectly

blue
^ sky (^) inserted word
       ( ]) after the last word

READING RATE AND ACCURACY

Total Words Read: _____

Number of Errors: _____

Number of Correct Words Read Per Minute (WPM): _____

Accuracy Rate: _____

(Number of Correct Words Read per Minute ÷ Total Words Read)

READING FLUENCY

	Low	Average	High
Decoding ability	○	○	○
Pace	○	○	○
Syntax	○	○	○
Self-correction	○	○	○
Intonation	○	○	○

Record student rates on the Oral Fluency Scores pages.

Name _____ Date _____ Score _____

The Case of the Gasping Garbage

Vocabulary

Read each item. Fill in the bubble for the answer you think is correct.

1. **Techniques** are

   Ⓐ methods. Ⓒ chances.

   Ⓑ openings. Ⓓ businesses.

2. An antonym for **peered** is

   Ⓐ wrote. Ⓒ explained.

   Ⓑ examined. Ⓓ glanced.

3. Doyle and Fossey are known throughout the fifth grade for their **pursuit** of answers. In this sentence, **pursuit** means

   Ⓐ explaining.

   Ⓑ studying.

   Ⓒ chasing.

   Ⓓ creating.

4. Frisco was a **competitor** of Drake's. A **competitor** is

   Ⓐ a classmate with better grades.

   Ⓑ someone who competes in a different sport.

   Ⓒ someone who sells the same product.

   Ⓓ an older person who teaches business skills.

5. Drake said he needed to simulate the same **environment.** Another word for **environment** is

   Ⓐ surroundings. Ⓒ ecology.

   Ⓑ nature. Ⓓ results.

The Case of the Gasping Garbage (continued)

Comprehension

Read the following questions carefully. Then completely fill in the bubble of each correct answer. You may look back at the selection to find the answer to each of the questions.

1. Who are Drake Doyle and Nell Fossey?

Ⓐ fifth-grade science detectives

Ⓑ owners of a catering business

Ⓒ famous scientific writers

Ⓓ teachers in a school

2. Why does Gabby Talberg call Doyle?

Ⓐ She needs his help with her science assignment.

Ⓑ She is making plans to meet at the mall later.

Ⓒ She has a monster in her garbage can.

Ⓓ She wants him to sample her father's new recipe.

The Case of the Gasping Garbage (continued)

3. What is Doyle's first rule of science?

Ⓐ Never remove the lid of a garbage can.

Ⓑ Do not let excitement overwhelm good sense.

Ⓒ Do not work on an empty stomach.

Ⓓ If you act in a calm manner, others will stay calm, too.

4. How does Mr. Doyle help Drake and Nell?

Ⓐ He helps them come up with their hypothesis.

Ⓑ He knows a scientific publisher.

Ⓒ He lets them stay up late to finish the project.

Ⓓ He provides equipment for the lab.

5. Why is Gabby Talberg disappointed?

Ⓐ Doyle and Fossey could not answer her question.

Ⓑ Yeast is not as exciting as a monster.

Ⓒ She wanted her dad's raisin bread for herself.

Ⓓ It is hard to get the ingredients used to recreate the experiment.

The Case of the Gasping Garbage (continued)

Read the following questions carefully. Use complete sentences to answer the questions. Possible answers below

6. What is the difference between James Frisco and Drake Doyle?

Frisco is a bad scientist who works alone; Doyle is a good one and has a partner.

7. Why is Fossey a good partner?

She is there when Doyle needs her, and she is prompt and efficient.

8. What are some of the clues that make Doyle and Fossey think there is not a monster in the garbage?

The garbage can is light and sounds hollow; the air nearby smells like bread.

9. How is the lab environment similar to the one in the Talberg garage?

The garbage is next to the heater so the temperature matches the garbage.

10. Why does the garbage can "burp"?

The "burp" is the can releasing carbon dioxide gas created by the yeast.

The Case of the Gasping Garbage (continued)

Read the question below. Write complete sentences for your answer. Support your answer with information from the selection.

Linking to the Concepts How might Doyle and Fossey repeat the experiment to be sure they were correct?

_____

_____

_____

_____

_____

Read the question below. Your answer should be based on your own experience. Write complete sentences for your answer.

Personal Response Write about a mystery you solved. How did you solve it?

_____

_____

_____

_____

_____

The Case of the Gasping Garbage (continued)

Grammar, Usage, and Mechanics

Read each question. Fill in the bubble beside the answer in each group that is correct. If none of the answers is correct, choose the last answer, "none of the above."

1. In which sentence do the subject and verb agree?

   Ⓐ Katia and Aaron usually raise the most money.

   Ⓑ Time pass quickly on vacation.

   Ⓒ The horse eat hay and oats in the barn.

   Ⓓ none of the above

2. In which sentence do the subject and verb agree?

   Ⓐ We calls each other.   Ⓒ They want cookies.

   Ⓑ We helps them.   Ⓓ none of the above

3. Which sentence has correct punctuation?

   Ⓐ The sky wasnt' clear; it looked like rain.

   Ⓑ The sky was'nt clear; it looked like rain.

   Ⓒ The sky wasn't clear; it looked like rain.

   Ⓓ none of the above

4. Which sentence has correct punctuation?

   Ⓐ Oranges, lemons, and limes are citrus fruits.

   Ⓑ Oranges, lemons and limes, are citrus fruits.

   Ⓒ Oranges, lemons, and limes, are citrus fruits.

   Ⓓ none of the above

5. Which sentence has a mistake in punctuation?

   Ⓐ Pablo eats hot dogs with mustard, relish, and onions.

   Ⓑ The goat, the pig, and the horse curled up in the barn.

   Ⓒ Mom planned to buy eggs, cereal, and milk.

   Ⓓ none of the above

The Case of the Gasping Garbage (continued)

Analyzing the Selection

Read the questions below. Write complete sentences for your answer. Support your answer with information from the selections.

Based on what you have read in this unit, what are some of the important principles of science? Why are they important?

_____

_____

_____

_____

_____

_____

_____

_____

_____

_____

_____

_____

_____

The Case of the Gasping Garbage (continued)

Oral Fluency Assessment

My Un-Birthday

Most of my friends think my family is a bit weird. We don't   1–13
celebrate birthdays. At least we don't celebrate them like most   14–23
people do. My friends say I have "un-birthday" parties.   24–32

It all started long ago. I think it was my grandmother's idea.   33–44
She and grandfather had grown up in Poland. They escaped   45–54
before World War II and made their way here.   55–63

When they got here, they were so happy that they decided   64–74
to share what they had with people who were not so lucky.   75–86
On their birthdays, they gave each other just one small gift.   87–97
Then they each bought a gift for someone who needed it more   98–109
than they did.   110–112

As the years passed and the family grew, the custom   113–122
continued. On my last birthday, I got a backpack for school. All   123–134
the other gifts were for students at the South School. This is a   135–147
school for young people who are very poor. When we walked in   148–159
with our arms full of gifts, everyone was excited. Seeing them   160–170
receive their gifts was the best birthday gift of all.   171–180

**EVALUATING CODES
FOR ORAL FLUENCY**

sky   (/) words read incorrectly

blue
^   sky   (^) inserted word
         ( ]) after the last word

READING RATE AND ACCURACY

Total Words Read: _____

Number of Errors: _____

Number of Correct Words
Read Per Minute (WPM):   _____

Accuracy Rate: _____

(Number of Correct Words Read per
Minute ÷ Total Words Read)

READING FLUENCY

	Low	Average	High
Decoding ability	○	○	○
Pace	○	○	○
Syntax	○	○	○
Self-correction	○	○	○
Intonation	○	○	○

Record student rates on the Oral Fluency Scores pages.

How Ben Franklin Stole the Lightning

Vocabulary

Read each item. Fill in the bubble for the answer you think is correct.

1. Which homograph best completes the sentences?

   I need an aluminum _____ for softball.

   We found a _____ living in our attic.

   Ⓐ pole   Ⓒ ball

   Ⓑ bat   Ⓓ duck

2. Another word for **genuine** is

   Ⓐ real.   Ⓒ expensive.

   Ⓑ ancient.   Ⓓ heavy.

3. One of the things Benjamin Franklin liked to do best was to create **inventions. Inventions** are

   Ⓐ paddles to help you swim faster.

   Ⓑ predictions about what the weather will be.

   Ⓒ types of sails.

   Ⓓ things that are made for the first time.

4. They ran an electric **charge** through it. In this sentence, **charge** means

   Ⓐ a thrill.   Ⓒ a command.

   Ⓑ a load of electricity.   Ⓓ a cost.

5. Two people got **shocked** by sparks. This means that the sparks

   Ⓐ jolted them.   Ⓒ carried them.

   Ⓑ surprised them.   Ⓓ avoided them.

How Ben Franklin Stole the Lightning (continued)

Comprehension

Read the following questions carefully. Then completely fill in the bubble of each correct answer. You may look back at the selection to find the answer to each of the questions.

1. Franklin was all of these EXCEPT

  Ⓐ a writer.

  Ⓑ a shopkeeper.

  Ⓒ a world traveler.

  Ⓓ a carpenter.

2. What did Franklin invent when he was eleven?

  Ⓐ a glass harmonica

  Ⓑ swim paddles

  Ⓒ a library chair

  Ⓓ daylight savings time

How Ben Franklin Stole the Lightning (continued)

3. Why did Franklin sail to England and France?

Ⓐ to do business for America

Ⓑ to figure out a shorter way across the ocean

Ⓒ to find a new market for his inventions

Ⓓ to take a break from his work

4. Which of these is a fact about Franklin?

Ⓐ Franklin was a very clever man.

Ⓑ Franklin enjoyed flying kites.

Ⓒ Franklin wrote an almanac.

Ⓓ Franklin was liked by most people who knew him.

5. Franklin believed that lightning

Ⓐ would be useful to people.

Ⓑ was pure electricity.

Ⓒ was very dangerous to work with.

Ⓓ could be created with a kite and silk ribbon.

How Ben Franklin Stole the Lightning (continued)

Read the following questions carefully. Use complete sentences to answer the questions. Possible answers below

6. What were some of Franklin's ideas about health?

   Exercise helps keep people fit; fresh air, water, and citrus fruits kept people healthy.

7. How is an electrician today different from one in Franklin's time?

   Electricians today are repairpeople; in Franklin's day, they did tricks.

8. What happened after Franklin charted the Gulf Stream?

   Sailors could follow its flow and travel across the Atlantic more quickly.

9. Why did Franklin invent the lightning rod?

   He invented it to save lives and property—lightning caused many fires in his time.

10. How did Franklin help end the Revolutionary War?

    He convinced France to fight with us and had Great Britain sign a treaty.

How Ben Franklin Stole the Lightning (continued)

Read the question below. Write complete sentences for your answer. Support your answer with information from the selection.

Linking to the Concepts What made Franklin a good scientist?

_____

_____

_____

_____

_____

Read the question below. Your answer should be based on your own experience. Write complete sentences for your answer.

Personal Response How would your life be different without Franklin's ideas and inventions?

_____

_____

_____

_____

_____

How Ben Franklin Stole the Lightning (continued)

Grammar, Usage, and Mechanics

Read each question. Fill in the bubble beside the answer in each group that is correct. If none of the answers is correct, choose the last answer, "none of the above."

1. Which sentence has a compound subject?

   Ⓐ A dog and a cat played. Ⓒ No one saw them.

   Ⓑ They stood waiting. Ⓓ none of the above

2. What is the best way to combine these two sentences?

   I like swimming best. My mom likes swimming best, too.

   Ⓐ I like swimming best: and my mom likes it best, too.

   Ⓑ My mom and I like swimming best.

   Ⓒ I like swimming best my mom also likes swimming.

   Ⓓ none of the above

3. Which sentence has a compound predicate?

   Ⓐ Matt wants to bake bread and take it to school.

   Ⓑ After he washes his hands, Mom shows him how.

   Ⓒ It needs to cool, so he puts it on a rack.

   Ⓓ none of the above

4. Which sentence has a compound predicate?

   Ⓐ The clothes and linens were dirty.

   Ⓑ Maria washed the linens and put them away.

   Ⓒ I washed the clothes later that day.

   Ⓓ none of the above

5. In which sentence is a demonstrative pronoun underlined?

   Ⓐ Did Yin get those on <u>his</u> vacation?

   Ⓑ Did Yin get those <u>on</u> his vacation?

   Ⓒ Did Yin get <u>those</u> on his vacation?

   Ⓓ none of the above

How Ben Franklin Stole the Lightning (continued)

Analyzing the Selection

Read the question below. Write complete sentences for your answer. Support your answer with information from the selection.

What do you think was Franklin's greatest contribution to America? Use information from the selection and your opinion to write an answer.

_____

_____

_____

_____

_____

_____

_____

_____

_____

_____

_____

_____

How Ben Franklin Stole the Lightning (continued)

Oral Fluency Assessment

Earthquake Myths

It can be scary when earthquakes happen. Ancient people
did not like them any more than we do. But these people did
not understand why they happened. So they made up stories to
explain why the ground shakes and trembles.

In India, many thought that eight elephants held up Earth.
When one got tired and lowered its head, the ground moved.
In Mongolia, the people there thought that a giant frog carried
Earth on its back. When it moved, the ground moved with it.
African stories pictured the Earth as part of a giant person.
When the giant moved, the ground moved.

Some Native Americans told tales about a huge turtle that
carried Earth on its back. It caused earthquakes when it swam.
One tale dealt with four bulls that held up Earth. When the bulls
got tired, they tossed the Earth back and forth.

Today we understand more about the Earth. We know that
the surface of the Earth is made of large plates. Earthquakes
happen when the plates grind together. Science may tell
us what earthquakes are. However, the old tales are
still interesting

1–9	
10–22	
23–33	
34–40	
41–50	
51–61	
62–72	
73–84	
85–95	
96–102	
103–112	
113–123	
124–136	
137–145	
146–155	
156–166	
167–175	
176–184	
185–186	

**EVALUATING CODES
FOR ORAL FLUENCY**

sky   (/) words read incorrectly

blue
^   sky   (^) inserted word
          ( ]) after the last word

READING RATE AND ACCURACY

Total Words Read: _____

Number of Errors: _____

Number of Correct Words
Read Per Minute (WPM):   _____

Accuracy Rate: _____

(Number of Correct Words Read per
Minute ÷ Total Words Read)

READING FLUENCY

	Low	Average	High
Decoding ability	○	○	○
Pace	○	○	○
Syntax	○	○	○
Self-correction	○	○	○
Intonation	○	○	○

Record student rates on the Oral Fluency Scores pages.

Name _____ Date _____ Score _____

How Fast Do You Eat Your Ice Cream?

Vocabulary

Read each item. Fill in the bubble for the answer you think is correct.

1. Something that is **common**

   Ⓐ happens often. Ⓒ makes noise.

   Ⓑ is invented. Ⓓ is useful.

2. Each of these examples is a comparative form EXCEPT

   Ⓐ faster. Ⓒ silliest.

   Ⓑ more confusing. Ⓓ pricier.

3. **Previous** researchers had studied "brain freeze." This means the researchers

   Ⓐ were earlier than others. Ⓒ had less education.

   Ⓑ were more skilled. Ⓓ kept careful records.

4. One scientist thought that "brain freeze" occurred in one-third of a **randomly** sampled population. This kind of population is

   Ⓐ not very fond of ice cream.

   Ⓑ mostly children.

   Ⓒ selected by chance.

   Ⓓ small in number.

5. The *Journal* initially **rejected** the paper. This means that the paper was

   Ⓐ edited. Ⓒ turned down.

   Ⓑ rewritten. Ⓓ reviewed by another scientist.

How Fast Do You Eat Your Ice Cream? (continued)

Comprehension

Read the following questions carefully. Then completely fill in the bubble of each correct answer. You may look back at the selection to find the answer to each of the questions.

1. Who is the author of this selection?

   Ⓐ a group of scientists studying headaches

   Ⓑ an ice cream maker

   Ⓒ a girl who likes ice cream

   Ⓓ the publisher of a scientific journal

2. Who is the author's sample population?

   Ⓐ frequent headache sufferers

   Ⓑ classmates

   Ⓒ people who eat a lot of ice cream

   Ⓓ shoppers at a drug store

How Fast Do You Eat Your Ice Cream? (continued)

3. What is the difference between the two test groups?

Ⓐ the speed they ate the ice cream

Ⓑ whether or not they had had headaches before

Ⓒ boys were in one group, girls were in the other

Ⓓ how much ice cream they were supposed to eat

4. Which of the variables in the chart is the same in both groups?

Ⓐ the percentage of females

Ⓑ the age of the subjects

Ⓒ the percentage with history of ice cream headaches

Ⓓ the percentage with regular headaches

5. The author initially created her project in order to

Ⓐ get famous at a young age.

Ⓑ pass a science class.

Ⓒ get published.

Ⓓ win an award at the science fair.

How Fast Do You Eat Your Ice Cream?(continued)

Read the following questions carefully. Use complete sentences to answer the questions. Possible answers below

6. What is the difference between what a scientist hypothesized and what the author thought?

The author thought "brain freeze" was more frequent than the scientist hypothesized.

7. Why did the author turn her project into an article?

She wants to prove the science fair judges wrong and challenge ideas about "brain freeze."

8. Why does the author include the information concerning her publication process?

She wants to show that getting published is not an easy process.

9. What did Reuter's News Agency think about the "brain freeze" article at first?

At first they thought a story about the study of "brain freeze" would be cute.

10. What happened as a result of the article being published?

The author and her findings became a popular news story.

UNIT 4 Lesson 5

How Fast Do You Eat Your Ice Cream? (continued)

Read the prompt below. Write complete sentences for your summary.

Linking to the Concepts Write a summary of this selection. Pretend you are writing it for a friend who has not read the selection.

_____

_____

_____

_____

_____

Read the question below. Your answer should be based on your own experience. Write complete sentences for your answer.

Personal Response What do you think of the author's research?

_____

_____

_____

_____

_____

How Fast Do You Eat Your Ice Cream?(continued)

Grammar, Usage, and Mechanics

Read each question. Fill in the bubble beside the answer in each group that is correct. If none of the answers is correct, choose the last answer, "none of the above."

1. Which answer is a complex sentence?

Ⓐ Tomorrow is the last day of school.

Ⓑ He did not have work for us; we had a party.

Ⓒ After we turn in our books, we can go home.

Ⓓ none of the above

2. Which answer is in the past tense?

Ⓐ Fans fill the stadium.　　Ⓒ Fans will fill the stadium.

Ⓑ Fans filled the stadium.　Ⓓ none of the above

3. Change this sentence from the present to the future tense.

Aunt Jen plants seeds and pulls weeds.

Ⓐ Aunt Jen planted seeds and pulled weeds.

Ⓑ Aunt Jen will plant seeds and pulls weeds.

Ⓒ Aunt Jen will plant seeds and pull weeds.

Ⓓ none of the above

4. Which answer is a complete sentence?

Ⓐ Several boats out.

Ⓑ Boats out of the harbor into the wide ocean.

Ⓒ Several boats out of the harbor into the ocean.

Ⓓ none of the above

5. Which answer is a run-on sentence?

Ⓐ Many people were waiting the store opened early.

Ⓑ They arrived early, and many shoppers had coupons.

Ⓒ Ties were on sale; however, bags were regular price.

Ⓓ none of the above

How Fast Do You Eat Your Ice Cream? (continued)

Analyzing the Selection

Read the question below. Write complete sentences for your answer. Support your answer with information from the selections.

Think about the good scientists, both young and adult, you have read about in this unit. What are some of the things they had in common that make them good scientists? Be sure to mention some of them by name and indicate their characteristics.

_____

_____

_____

_____

_____

_____

_____

_____

_____

_____

How Fast Do You Eat Your Ice Cream? (continued)

Oral Fluency Assessment

The Hills Get a Computer

Kate could not wait to get home. Today the family was   1–11
getting a computer. When school was over, she ran right home.   12–22
Kate burst through the door, stopped to pet her dog, and then   23–34
she ran into the den.   35–39
   There on the table in the corner was a computer. Kate's   40–50
mother had just taken it out of the box. She was connecting all   51–63
of the parts together. Mrs. Hill asked Kate if she wanted to help.   64–76
Kate quickly said "Yes!" and ran over to her mother.   77–86
   Kate was very careful to do exactly what her mother said.   87–97
She connected the keyboard and the monitor, the thing that   98–107
looks like a television, to the computer. Her mother checked all   108–118
the wires and only then plugged it into the wall.   119–128
   Mrs. Hill smiled at her daughter who seemed both excited   129–138
and nervous. Kate slowly moved her hand near the computer,   139–148
stuck her finger out, and pressed the START button.   149–157
   "Mom, this is exactly what we have at school! I already know   158–169
how to use it."   170–173
   "I'm glad you do, Kate. When Dad comes home, maybe you   174–184
can give us both a lesson."   185–190

**EVALUATING CODES
FOR ORAL FLUENCY**

sky   (/) words read incorrectly

blue
^ sky   (^) inserted word
            ( ]) after the last word

READING RATE AND ACCURACY

Total Words Read: _____

Number of Errors: _____

Number of Correct Words
Read Per Minute (WPM): _____

Accuracy Rate: _____

(Number of Correct Words Read per
Minute ÷ Total Words Read)

READING FLUENCY

	Low	Average	High
Decoding ability	○	○	○
Pace	○	○	○
Syntax	○	○	○
Self-correction	○	○	○
Intonation	○	○	○

Record student rates on the Oral Fluency Scores pages.

Name _____ **Date** _____ **Score** _____

Expository Writing

Writing Situation
A science fact or discovery

Audience
Students your age

Directions for Writing
Think of a science topic that you know, such as the sun, a certain plant or animal, or an interesting discovery. Explain this topic in a way that is accurate and interesting.

Checklist
You will earn the best score if you
- think about your topic and plan your writing before you begin.
- have a beginning paragraph that gets the attention of readers.
- describe the science topic clearly in an opening paragraph.
- explain why the topic is important to you.
- write in a way that will make the topic interesting to your readers.
- stay on the topic you chose.
- vary your sentences and the words you use.
- use subjects, verbs, and modifiers correctly.
- choose words that mean what you want to say.
- read your writing after you finish and check for mistakes.

Four Point Rubrics for Expository Writing

	1 Point	2 Points	3 Points	4 Points
Genre				
Expository	Composition has no introduction or clear topic. It offers a group of loosely related facts or a series of poorly written steps. No conclusion is included.	Composition is clearly organized around main points with supportive facts or assertions. Composition has no clear introduction, but its topic is identifiable. However, it includes many facts unrelated to the topic, or it describes things in a disorganized way. No conclusion is included.	Main points and supportive details can be identified, but they are not clearly marked. Composition has an introduction and offers facts about the topic. Some facts may be irrelevant, or some ideas may be vague or out of order. The report is fairly well organized but doesn't have a strong conclusion.	Traces and constructs a line of argument, identifying part-to-whole relations. Main points are supported with logical and appropriate evidence. Composition begins with an introduction and offers relevant facts about the topic or describes the topic appropriately. The report is organized using cause/effect, comparison/contrast, or another pattern. It ends with a strong conclusion.
Writing Traits				
Focus	Topic is unclear or wanders and must be inferred. Extraneous material may be present.	Topic/position/direction is unclear and must be inferred.	Topic/position is stated and direction/purpose is previewed and maintained. Mainly stays on topic.	Topic/position is clearly stated, previewed, and maintained throughout the paper. Topics and details are tied together with a central theme or purpose that is maintained/threaded throughout the paper.
Ideas/Content	Superficial and/or minimal content is included.	Main ideas are understandable, although they may be overly broad or simplistic, and the results may not be effective. Supporting detail is limited, insubstantial, overly general or off topic.	The writing is clear and focused. The reader can easily understand the main ideas. Support is present, although it may be limited or rather general.	Writing is exceptionally clear, focused, and interesting. Main ideas stand out and are developed by strong support and rich details.
Elaboration (supporting details and examples that develop the main idea)	States ideas or points with minimal detail to support them.	Includes sketchy, redundant, or general details; some may be irrelevant. Support for key ideas is very uneven.	Includes mix of general statements and specific details/examples. Support is mostly relevant but may be uneven and lack depth in places.	Includes specific details and supporting examples for each key point/idea. May use compare/contrast to support.
Writing Conventions				
Conventions Overall	Numerous errors in usage, grammar, spelling, capitalization, and punctuation repeatedly distract the reader and make the text difficult to read. The reader finds it difficult to focus on the message.	The writing demonstrates limited control of standard writing conventions (punctuation, spelling, capitalization, grammar, and usage). Errors sometimes impede readability.	The writing demonstrates control of standard writing conventions (punctuation, spelling, capitalization, grammar, and usage). Minor errors, while perhaps noticeable, do not impede readability.	The writing demonstrates exceptionally strong control of standard writing conventions (punctuation, spelling, capitalization, grammar, and usage) and uses them effectively to enhance communication. Errors are so few and so minor that the reader can easily skim over them.

Name _____ Date _____ Score _____

The Golden Spike

Vocabulary

Read each item. Fill in the bubble for the answer you think is correct.

1. The Greek root **geo** means
  Ⓐ time.   Ⓒ earth.
  Ⓑ light.   Ⓓ study of.

2. Another word for **assistance** is
  Ⓐ help.   Ⓒ work.
  Ⓑ sleep.   Ⓓ delay.

3. Promontory, Utah, was **buzzing** with activity. This means that the town
  Ⓐ was just starting out.
  Ⓑ was very active.
  Ⓒ had many jobs available.
  Ⓓ had people moving out.

4. A worker was **hastily** summoned. **Hastily** means about the same as
  Ⓐ loudly.
  Ⓑ eventually.
  Ⓒ formally.
  Ⓓ quickly.

5. The two **locomotives** inched toward one another. **Locomotives** are
  Ⓐ wild animals.   Ⓒ roads.
  Ⓑ train tracks.   Ⓓ train engines.

The Golden Spike (continued)

Comprehension

Read the following questions carefully. Then completely fill in the bubble of each correct answer. You may look back at the selection to find the answer to each of the questions.

1. Where does the selection take place?

   Ⓐ Nebraska

   Ⓑ Utah

   Ⓒ California

   Ⓓ New York

2. What made the crowd laugh at the celebration?

   Ⓐ They have been told funny stories.

   Ⓑ The band members are wearing silly hats.

   Ⓒ The executives cannot hit the spike.

   Ⓓ They are happy about the railroad being completed.

The Golden Spike (continued)

3. Which of these is a fact about the transcontinental railroad?

Ⓐ The railroad took eight years to complete.

Ⓑ The railroad made a vast country one.

Ⓒ The railroad changed life in America.

Ⓓ America would not be what it is today without it.

4. What happens right after Thomas Durant swung his hammer and missed?

Ⓐ A band begins to play.

Ⓑ A worker is summoned.

Ⓒ A railroad executive makes a speech.

Ⓓ Two locomotives inch toward one another.

5. The author wrote this selection to

Ⓐ help readers learn about how our country was formed.

Ⓑ tell about how difficult it is to build a transcontinental railroad.

Ⓒ inform us that Americans did not build the railroad.

Ⓓ tell about how locomotives work.

The Golden Spike (continued)

Read the following questions carefully. Use complete sentences to answer the questions. Possible answers below

6. What types of people are in the crowd?

Reporters, a band, executives, and the men who had built the railroad

7. What is the difference between how the Central Pacific Line and the Union Pacific Railroad worked on the project?

The Central Pacific started west and built east; the Union Pacific started east and built west.

8. What does it mean that "the country cheered as one"?

People were excited to have the railroad finished and the nation connected.

9. Before the railroad, what opinion did Americans have of the West?

They thought it was untamed land populated by Native Americans.

10. How did life change after the railroad was complete?

Goods had a new way to get to market; settlers went west; and western cities grew.

The Golden Spike (continued)

Read the question below. Write complete sentences for your answer. Support your answer with information from the selection.

Linking to the Concepts Why do you think everyone made such a fuss about the completion of the transcontinental railroad?

_____

_____

_____

_____

_____

Read the question below. Your answer should be based on your own experience. Write complete sentences for your answer.

Personal Response Suppose you had been present at the celebration. What would you have thought?

_____

_____

_____

_____

_____

The Golden Spike (continued)

Grammar, Usage, and Mechanics

Read each question. Fill in the bubble beside the answer in each group that is correct. If none of the answers is correct, choose the last answer, "none of the above."

1. In which sentence is a preposition underlined?
   Ⓐ Vance's cat <u>crawled</u> under the porch.
   Ⓑ Vance's cat crawled under <u>the</u> porch.
   Ⓒ Vance's cat crawled <u>under</u> the porch.
   Ⓓ none of the above

2. In which sentence is a prepositional phrase underlined?
   Ⓐ Nets <u>at the gym</u> are old.　　Ⓒ Nets at the gym <u>are old</u>.
   Ⓑ <u>Nets</u> at the gym are old.　　Ⓓ none of the above

3. Which item is in the past tense?
   Ⓐ Anton will buy every book.
   Ⓑ Anton bought every book.
   Ⓒ Anton buys every book.
   Ⓓ none of the above

4. In which sentence is the underlined word modified by a prepositional phrase?
   Ⓐ The cat with the <u>orange</u> stripes is larger than mine.
   Ⓑ The cat with the orange stripes is <u>larger</u> than mine.
   Ⓒ The cat with the orange stripes is larger than <u>mine</u>.
   Ⓓ none of the above

5. Which pronoun can replace the object of the preposition?
   Noreen drew a picture on the tablet.
   Ⓐ she
   Ⓑ it
   Ⓒ her
   Ⓓ none of the above

The Golden Spike (continued)

Analyzing the Selection

Read the question below. Write complete sentences for your answer. Support your answer with information from the selection.

Why was the transcontinental railroad so important to the future of the United States?

_____

_____

_____

_____

_____

_____

_____

_____

_____

_____

_____

_____

_____

The Golden Spike (continued)

Oral Fluency Assessment

The Zipper

For a long time, buttons were used to close up clothing and	1–12
shoes. Elias Howe, the inventor of the sewing machine, had a	13–23
better idea. He came up with a plan for a special closer. But he	24–37
never did much to sell his idea.	38–44
Forty-four years later, Will Johnson invented the clasp	45–53
locker. He began a company to make these closers. He even	54–64
showed them at the World's Fair. No one showed any real	65–75
interest in his work. His closer was used only on things like	76–87
boots and bags.	88–90
Gil Shore worked at Johnson's company. He changed the	91–99
teeth on the clasp locker. A company that made boots liked	100–110
this idea. They called it the "zipper." They put it on their boots.	111–123
People liked it. Now they could zip their boots with one hand.	124–135
Until the 1930s, zippers were not used on clothing. Then ads	136–146
showed children's clothes with zippers. Parents liked the idea.	147–155
Their children now could dress themselves! Soon companies	156–163
began using them on adult clothing. Now you find them on	164–174
almost everything.	175–176

**EVALUATING CODES
FOR ORAL FLUENCY**

sky   (/) words read incorrectly

blue
 ^   sky   (^) inserted word
          ( ]) after the last word

READING RATE AND ACCURACY

Total Words Read: _____

Number of Errors: _____

Number of Correct Words
Read Per Minute (WPM):   _____

Accuracy Rate: _____

(Number of Correct Words Read per
Minute ÷ Total Words Read)

READING FLUENCY

	Low	Average	High
Decoding ability	○	○	○
Pace	○	○	○
Syntax	○	○	○
Self-correction	○	○	○
Intonation	○	○	○

Record student rates on the Oral Fluency Scores pages.

Name _____ Date _____ Score _____

John Henry Races the Steam Drill

Vocabulary

Read each item. Fill in the bubble for the answer you think is correct.

1. Another word for **generous** is

  Ⓐ busy.   Ⓒ unselfish.

  Ⓑ thrifty.   Ⓓ manageable.

2. The Latin root ***rupt*** in the word *rupture* means

  Ⓐ break.   Ⓒ write.

  Ⓑ conquer.   Ⓓ build.

3. His wife told John Henry not to **strain** himself. In this sentence, **strain** means

  Ⓐ to think too highly of yourself.

  Ⓑ to get hurt by doing too much.

  Ⓒ to travel too far away from home.

  Ⓓ to upset yourself.

4. Folklore experts began to study the John Henry **legend** seriously in the 1920s. A **legend** is a type of

  Ⓐ record.

  Ⓑ story.

  Ⓒ song.

  Ⓓ family.

5. There are one hundred **versions** of the ballad. **Versions** are

  Ⓐ verses.

  Ⓑ authors.

  Ⓒ singers.

  Ⓓ variations.

John Henry Races the Steam Drill (continued)

Comprehension

Read the following questions carefully. Then completely fill in the bubble of each correct answer. You may look back at the selection to find the answer to each of the questions.

1. What was the Big Bend Tunnel?

Ⓐ the tunnel under the English Channel

Ⓑ a subway tunnel in New York City

Ⓒ a railroad tunnel through mountains

Ⓓ a tunnel made by Captain Tommy

2. What is the sound of John Henry's hammer like?

Ⓐ a crash of thunder

Ⓑ the splashing of waves

Ⓒ a lion's roar

Ⓓ the hum of a car's motor

John Henry Races the Steam Drill (continued)

3. What does the selection say John Henry always did while driving steel?

Ⓐ He challenged his fellow workers to races.

Ⓑ He stopped frequently to rest.

Ⓒ He drank lots of water.

Ⓓ He sang.

4. What conclusion can you draw about Captain Tommy's offer of the money and the suit?

Ⓐ He does not think John Henry can win.

Ⓑ He wants steam drills to replace steel drivers.

Ⓒ He wants to encourage John Henry to win.

Ⓓ He wants to make Polly Ann happy.

5. What happens to the suit of clothes that John Henry wins?

Ⓐ They will be given to Captain Tommy.

Ⓑ He wears them to a party the next weekend.

Ⓒ His wife gives them to her brother.

Ⓓ He is buried in them.

John Henry Races the Steam Drill (continued)

Read the following questions carefully. Use complete sentences to answer the questions. Possible answers below

6. What is the difference between what the company men and the steel driving men think will happen in the contest?

The company men think John Henry has no chance, but the steel drivers think he can win.

7. Why does John Henry ask for a new hammer?

His old one is feeling too light and he wants a heavier one so he can win.

8. Why does John Henry name his new hammer Polly Ann?

John Henry names his new hammer in honor of his wife.

9. Why does John Henry die at the end of the selection?

He pushes himself too hard in the contest and his heart gives out.

10. What is different about how John Henry dies in the selection and how the real John Henry probably died?

The real John Henry probably died in an accident, and not after a contest.

John Henry Races the Steam Drill (continued)

Read the question below. Write complete sentences for your answer. Support your answer with information from the selection.

Linking to the Concepts Why are so many people interested in the competition between a person and a machine?

_____

_____

_____

_____

_____

Read the question below. Your answer should be based on your own experience. Write complete sentences for your answer.

Personal Response What was the most difficult job you have ever had to do? Explain what made it so hard to do.

_____

_____

_____

_____

_____

John Henry Races the Steam Drill (continued)

Grammar, Usage, and Mechanics

Read each pair of sentences. Fill in the bubble beside the answer that is the best way to combine the sentences.

1. The bug jumped. The bug was on the table.

Ⓐ The bug jumped and the bug was on the table.

Ⓑ The bug on the table jumped.

Ⓒ The bug a table jumped.

Ⓓ none of the above

2. The phone rang. The phone was in the den.

Ⓐ The phone in the den rang.

Ⓑ The den rang phone.

Ⓒ The phone rang was in the den.

Ⓓ none of the above

3. The garden has flowers. The garden is behind the house.

Ⓐ The garden behind the house has flowers.

Ⓑ The garden has flowers and behind the house.

Ⓒ The garden is behind the house: and it has flowers.

Ⓓ none of the above

4. The grass was food. The grass was in the meadow.

Ⓐ The grass was food it was in the meadow.

Ⓑ The grass was food and in the meadow.

Ⓒ The grass in the meadow was food.

Ⓓ none of the above

5. She saw Ann at the park. She saw Jim at the park.

Ⓐ She saw the park.

Ⓑ She saw them at the park.

Ⓒ Ann and Jim saw her.

Ⓓ none of the above

John Henry Races the Steam Drill (continued)

Analyzing the Selection

Read the question below. Write complete sentences for your answer. Support your answer with information from the selection.

Throughout history, machines have replaced humans to do many jobs. What are the good and bad results of this? Use information from the selection, things you already know, and your opinion when you write.

_____

_____

_____

_____

_____

_____

_____

_____

_____

_____

_____

_____

John Henry Races the Steam Drill (continued)

Oral Fluency Assessment

Kayaking

A kayak is a small boat. It was invented by the native people	1–13
in Alaska and northern Canada. The boats were made of animal	14–24
skins. The hide was wrapped around a wooden frame and	25–34
sealed. They were used to hunt and fish in the ocean.	35–45
People today use kayaks for fun. They call their sport	46–55
kayaking. It is a sport that is enjoyed by people all over the	56–68
world. It is even in the Olympics!	69–75
The safest way to learn to kayak is to take lessons. Centers	76–87
around the country teach you the sport. They will have	88–97
everything you will need. You will learn in a safe body of water,	98–110
such as a pool.	111–114
Once your skills improve, you can rent a boat and try it on	115–127
your own. You will want to start in a calm river or lake. As you	128–142
get better at it, you can move up to faster waters.	143–153
Here is a surprise. Kayaking can be enjoyed in cities! Even	154–164
in the large cities in the East, kayakers are having lots of fun in	165–178
local rivers.	179–180

**EVALUATING CODES
FOR ORAL FLUENCY**

sky   (/) words read incorrectly

blue
^   sky   (^) inserted word
         ( ]) after the last word

READING RATE AND ACCURACY

Total Words Read: _____

Number of Errors: _____

Number of Correct Words
Read Per Minute (WPM):   _____

Accuracy Rate: _____

(Number of Correct Words Read per
Minute ÷ Total Words Read)

READING FLUENCY

	Low	Average	High
Decoding ability	○	○	○
Pace	○	○	○
Syntax	○	○	○
Self-correction	○	○	○
Intonation	○	○	○

Record student rates on the Oral Fluency Scores pages.

Name _____ **Date** _____ **Score** _____

Immigrant Children

Vocabulary

Read each item. Fill in the bubble for the answer you think is correct.

1. **Yearning** means about the same as

   Ⓐ crying.   Ⓒ planning.

   Ⓑ shouting.   Ⓓ wishing.

2. A synonym for **dreaded** is

   Ⓐ disliked.   Ⓒ avoided.

   Ⓑ feared.   Ⓓ appreciated.

3. At the entry ports, helpers **translated** many questions and answers. This means the helpers

   Ⓐ changed words from one language into another.

   Ⓑ spoke at a very rapid pace.

   Ⓒ suggested questions the immigrants should ask.

   Ⓓ helped immigrants write answers.

4. Some immigrants demanded better **wages. Wages** are

   Ⓐ kitchen facilities.

   Ⓑ behavior by bosses.

   Ⓒ jobs.

   Ⓓ pay for work.

5. Unions organized marches and held **strikes. Strikes** are

   Ⓐ signs.

   Ⓑ child workers.

   Ⓒ work stoppages.

   Ⓓ musical instruments.

Immigrant Children (continued)

Comprehension

Read the following questions carefully. Then completely fill in the bubble of each correct answer. You may look back at the selection to find the answer to each of the questions.

1. Where was the busiest station for immigrants located?

   (A) San Francisco

   (B) Chicago

   (C) Ellis Island

   (D) Miami

2. Why were immigrants marked on their clothes with chalk?

   (A) The chalk markings told inspectors what country the immigrant was from.

   (B) The markings told where in the inspection process the immigrant was.

   (C) Some immigrants were marked with chalk if they already had jobs.

   (D) A mark on an immigrant's back meant the person might have a disease.

Immigrant Children (continued)

3. What happened to the immigrants after their eye exam?

Ⓐ They faced an inspector.

Ⓑ They went to the island hospital.

Ⓒ They were put onto ferries.

Ⓓ They were sent home.

4. Why did both immigrants and native-born Americans go west after 1862?

Ⓐ The cities in the West had more jobs.

Ⓑ They had heard that buffalo hunting was profitable.

Ⓒ They wanted to claim free land.

Ⓓ They were looking for gold.

5. The selection is written from what point of view?

Ⓐ first-person point of view

Ⓑ third-person point of view

Ⓒ second-person point of view

Ⓓ from the point of view of Ellis Island

Immigrant Children (continued)

Read the following questions carefully. Use complete sentences to answer the questions. Possible answers below

6. Why did many immigrants come to the United States?

They came here for a better life.

7. How was coming to America for immigrants like going to the moon?

Both trips involve traveling great distances to unknown places.

8. Why did so many immigrants from Sweden and Norway often settle in the Midwest?

The weather in the Midwest reminded them of home.

9. What event caused states to pass laws against child labor?

A deadly factory fire in New York City led to laws against child labor.

10. What happened to immigrants who failed inspection?

They had to leave the United States and take a ship overseas.

Immigrant Children (continued)

Read the question below. Write complete sentences for your answer. Support your answer with information from the selection.

Linking to the Concepts How was life harder for immigrants once they arrived in the United States?

_____

_____

_____

_____

_____

_____

Read the questions below. Your answer should be based on your own experience. Write complete sentences for your answer.

Personal Response Suppose you had landed at Ellis Island. What would you have thought? What would have made you happy, and what would have worried you?

_____

_____

_____

_____

_____

_____

Immigrant Children (continued)

Grammar, Usage, and Mechanics

Read each pair of sentences. Fill in the bubble beside the answer that is the best way to combine the sentences.

1. Bob baked the potatoes. Bill made the salad.

Ⓐ Bob baked the potatoes; and Bill made the salad.

Ⓑ Bob baked the potatoes and Bill made the salad.

Ⓒ Bob baked the potatoes, and Bill made the salad.

Ⓓ none of the above

2. I have piano lessons. The lessons are in the school.

Ⓐ The school lessons are in piano.

Ⓑ I have piano lessons in the school.

Ⓒ I have piano lessons; in the school.

Ⓓ none of the above

3. Fred now has two teeth. Fred is my baby brother.

Ⓐ Fred, my baby brother, now has two teeth.

Ⓑ Fred my baby brother now has two teeth.

Ⓒ Fred now has two teeth, Fred is my baby brother.

Ⓓ none of the above

4. Mom washed. Dad dried.

Ⓐ Mom washed and Dad dried.

Ⓒ Mom washed: and Dad dried.

Ⓑ Mom washed; and Dad dried.

Ⓓ none of the above

5. Grace wanted to sit up front. Lin was already there.

Ⓐ Grace wanted to sit up front but Lin was already there.

Ⓑ Grace wanted to sit up front, but Lin was already there.

Ⓒ Grace wanted. To sit up front but, Lin was already there.

Ⓓ none of the above

Immigrant Children (continued)

Analyzing the Selection

Read the question below. Write complete sentences for your answer. Support your answer with information from the selections.

Think about the first three selections in this unit. How did some of the people in the selections contribute to making the United States a great nation?

_____

_____

_____

_____

_____

_____

_____

_____

_____

_____

_____

_____

_____

_____

Immigrant Children (continued)

Oral Fluency Assessment

The Cactus

Joe and his family were on vacation in Mexico. They had
visited the local markets and explored the ruins. They even
had gone fishing. It was an exciting and fun vacation.

One day, they drove out to the desert. They went in the early
morning. The family took a shade tent with them. They also
took plenty of water. Joe had read about the cactus at school
for a report. He wanted to see as many cacti as he could. He
knew that there are over two thousand types. More types of
cactus grow in Mexico than anywhere else in the world.

Even early in the day, it was hot. Joe and his family admired
the pretty cactus flowers. "They don't look like other flowers
I've ever seen," said his mother. His younger sister added, "Look
at all the different colors: red, orange, purple, white, brown,
and pink."

Joe said, "Did you know that the cactus has fruit? Many of
them taste good, too."

"Ouch! You would have to get past those awful stickers first,"
laughed his sister.

1–11
12–21
22–31
32–44
45–55
56–67
68–81
82–92
93–102
103–115
116–125
126–136
137–146
147–148
149–160
161–164
165–175
176–178

**EVALUATING CODES
FOR ORAL FLUENCY**

sky   (/) words read incorrectly

blue
  ^ sky   (^) inserted word
            ( ]) after the last word

READING RATE AND ACCURACY

Total Words Read: _____

Number of Errors: _____

Number of Correct Words
Read Per Minute (WPM):   _____

Accuracy Rate: _____

(Number of Correct Words Read per
Minute ÷ Total Words Read)

READING FLUENCY

	Low	Average	High
Decoding ability	○	○	○
Pace	○	○	○
Syntax	○	○	○
Self-correction	○	○	○
Intonation	○	○	○

Record student rates on the Oral Fluency Scores pages.

Name _____ Date _____ Score _____

The Dust Bowl

Vocabulary

Read each item. Fill in the bubble for the answer you think is correct.

1. An **era** is

Ⓐ a machine.

Ⓒ a period of history.

Ⓑ a road.

Ⓓ a large wheat field.

2. What is the superlative form of the adjective *sad*?

Ⓐ more sadder

Ⓒ saddest

Ⓑ most saddest

Ⓓ sadder

3. The item was in high **demand.** This means people

Ⓐ were tired of the item.

Ⓑ could not afford the item.

Ⓒ could not sell the item.

Ⓓ really wanted the item.

4. Homeless families camped out by roadsides and irrigation **ditches. Ditches** are

Ⓐ fields with crops.

Ⓑ forests with mostly older trees.

Ⓒ channels for water.

Ⓓ large barns.

5. Camps gave migrants a place where they could feel safe from unfriendly **locals.** What are **locals?**

Ⓐ people who have lived in a place for a long time

Ⓑ fierce and dangerous bears

Ⓒ farm bosses

Ⓓ border officers

The Dust Bowl (continued)

Comprehension

Read the following questions carefully. Then completely fill in the bubble of each correct answer. You may look back at the selection to find the answer to each of the questions.

1. Which of these states was NOT part of the Dust Bowl?

   Ⓐ Maine

   Ⓑ Colorado

   Ⓒ Kansas

   Ⓓ Oklahoma

2. How was the soil on the Great Plains like chocolate?

   Ⓐ It was sweet to smell.

   Ⓑ It broke into square chunks.

   Ⓒ It was dark brown.

   Ⓓ It could grow many kinds of crops.

The Dust Bowl (continued)

3. What happened after World War I?

Ⓐ Ranchers and farmers made more money.

Ⓑ Grassland covered the Great Plains.

Ⓒ The price of farm products dropped.

Ⓓ Farmers were not able to plow as much land.

4. What happened on "Black Tuesday"?

Ⓐ the first major dust storm

Ⓑ the stock market crash

Ⓒ the beginning of World War I

Ⓓ the death of the President

5. The author wrote this selection in order to

Ⓐ convince the reader that the Dust Bowl could happen today.

Ⓑ explain why grass is as important as crops.

Ⓒ show how the Dust Bowl changed the country.

Ⓓ tell about a family who survived the Dust Bowl.

The Dust Bowl (continued)

Read the following questions carefully. Use complete sentences to answer the questions. Possible answers below

6. How was the farmland destroyed in the 1930s?

People overused the land. Little grass was left to hold the soil.

7. Why did farm production increase during World War I?

It increased because the nation needed grain and beef to supply the troops.

8. How was farming different after 1930?

Mechanical farm equipment made farming faster and easier.

9. Why did the wind storms hurt the farmers so badly?

The storms occurred in spring, and blew away new plants, seeds and soil.

10. Why did the Farm Security Administration start camps for migrant workers?

The camps were necessary because the workers often had no place to live.

The Dust Bowl (continued)

Read the question below. Write complete sentences for your answer. Support your answer with information from the selection.

Linking to the Concepts How did the Dust Bowl change the nation?

_____

_____

_____

_____

_____

_____

Read the question below. Your answer should be based on your own experience. Write complete sentences for your answer.

Personal Response What would you have done to make Dust Bowl victims welcome in your state?

_____

_____

_____

_____

_____

_____

The Dust Bowl (continued)

Grammar, Usage, and Mechanics

Read each question. Fill in the bubble beside the answer in each group that is correct. If none of the answers is correct, choose the last answer, "none of the above."

1. In which sentence are the verbs correct?

Ⓐ The picnic was at noon, and the game started later.

Ⓑ The picnic will be at noon, and the game has started later.

Ⓒ The picnic will be at noon, and the game started later.

Ⓓ none of the above

2. In which sentence are the verbs correct?

Ⓐ We went to the gym, and then some of us ride to the park.

Ⓑ We went to the gym, and then some of us rode to the park.

Ⓒ We will go to the gym, and then some of us rode to the park.

Ⓓ none of the above

3. Which item is a complete sentence?

Ⓐ The yellow giraffe.   Ⓒ Eats leaves.

Ⓑ The giraffe eats leaves.   Ⓓ none of the above

4. Which item is a fragment?

Ⓐ A kangaroo rat here.

Ⓑ Cactus plants have flowers.

Ⓒ A flock of birds visits us.

Ⓓ none of the above

5. Which sentence begins with a dependent clause?

Ⓐ These make better colors than the old markers.

Ⓑ We flew, and we rented a car.

Ⓒ While on vacation, I saw the ocean.

Ⓓ none of the above

The Dust Bowl (continued)

Analyzing the Selection

Read the question below. Write complete sentences for your answer. Support your answer with information from the selection.

You read earlier how the transcontinental railroad and immigration changed the United States. How did the stock market crash and the Dust Bowl change the nation, both immediately and years after? Use information from the selection and your prior knowledge to write your answer.

_____

_____

_____

_____

_____

_____

_____

_____

_____

_____

_____

_____

_____

The Dust Bowl (continued)

Oral Fluency Assessment

The Gold Dogs

How would you like to earn your living jumping out of	1–11
airplanes? The Gold Dogs do just that. They are a special group	12–23
of Army paratroopers who perform at air shows.	24–31
All Army soldiers who jump with parachutes must be in good	32–42
shape. They go through long training to learn how to jump and	43–54
how to land. When they are training, they jump with heavy	55–65
packs. This is because they might have to take food or other	66–77
supplies to soldiers on the ground.	78–83
After they jump from the airplane, they pull a special cord	84–94
that opens the parachute. It is like a big cloth bag, open at	95–107
the bottom. It lets the jumper float down to the ground. There	108–119
is a great deal of skill needed to jump, land, and repack the	120–132
parachute. Repacking is very important. You must do it right so	133–143
that it will open the next time it is used.	144–153
The Gold Dogs wear gold-colored jump suits and shiny	154–163
black boots. They are very proud of what they do for the Army.	164–176
People enjoy seeing them at air shows. When young people see	177–187
them, they want to become a Gold Dog.	188–195

**EVALUATING CODES
FOR ORAL FLUENCY**

sky (/) words read incorrectly

blue
^ sky (^) inserted word
( ]) after the last word

READING RATE AND ACCURACY

Total Words Read: _____

Number of Errors: _____

Number of Correct Words
Read Per Minute (WPM): _____

Accuracy Rate: _____

(Number of Correct Words Read per
Minute ÷ Total Words Read)

READING FLUENCY

	Low	Average	High
Decoding ability	○	○	○
Pace	○	○	○
Syntax	○	○	○
Self-correction	○	○	○
Intonation	○	○	○

Record student rates on the Oral Fluency Scores pages.

Name _____ Date _____ Score _____

Pop's Bridge

Vocabulary

Read each item. Fill in the bubble for the answer you think is correct.

1. What is the correct contraction for the underlined words in the sentence?

We are going to visit our uncle during spring break.

Ⓐ Were Ⓒ Wer'e

Ⓑ We're Ⓓ We'are

2. When you are **ashamed,** you are

Ⓐ embarrassed. Ⓒ concerned.

Ⓑ ill. Ⓓ satisfied.

3. The author looks for his dad through **binoculars. Binoculars** are

Ⓐ powerful sunglasses.

Ⓑ a pair of holes in a fence.

Ⓒ a tool for seeing far away.

Ⓓ long rows of very tall buildings.

4. Sailboats **skim** on the water. **Skim** means the boats

Ⓐ pull water skiers.

Ⓑ attract fish.

Ⓒ cause damage.

Ⓓ move swiftly and lightly.

5. The author is able to **slip** a puzzle piece into his pocket. This means that he puts the puzzle piece into his pocket

Ⓐ eventually. Ⓒ noisily.

Ⓑ secretly. Ⓓ delicately.

Pop's Bridge (continued)

Comprehension

Read the following questions carefully. Then completely fill in the bubble of each correct answer. You may look back at the selection to find the answer to each of the questions.

1. Who are the "skywalkers"?

Ⓐ painters

Ⓑ tightrope walkers

Ⓒ high-iron men

Ⓓ pilots

2. Who is the narrator of this selection?

Ⓐ the child of a skywalker

Ⓑ someone who worked on a bridge similar to the Golden Gate Bridge

Ⓒ the architect of the Golden Gate Bridge

Ⓓ the wife of a painter

Pop's Bridge (continued)

3. The Golden Gate Bridge is best described as

Ⓐ a great construction feat.

Ⓑ a surprising natural event.

Ⓒ a step in the expansion of America.

Ⓓ a building that was difficult to make.

4. Why are there no cars allowed on the bridge on opening day?

Ⓐ The bridge was not strong enough to hold cars.

Ⓑ There was a big celebration.

Ⓒ The roadway on the bridge was not complete.

Ⓓ Cars were not yet invented.

5. How are Charlie's dad and Robert's dad similar?

Ⓐ Both are glad to have the bridge finished.

Ⓑ Both are not very good at puzzles.

Ⓒ Both are injured in an accident at the bridge.

Ⓓ Both risk their lives to work on the bridge.

Pop's Bridge (continued)

Read the following questions carefully. Use complete sentences to answer the questions. Possible answers below

6. Who are the men the narrator names at the end of the selection "who worked together to build the most beautiful bridge in the world"?

The narrator names laborers, riveters, carpenters, painters, and skywalkers.

7. What does the narrator think of the skywalkers?

He thinks they have the most important job on the Golden Gate Bridge.

8. What is the terrible thing that happens in the selection to change the narrator's mind?

A fatal accident makes him see that everyone shares the same risk.

9. Why do the narrator's hands sweat on foggy days?

He worries because he cannot see if his father is safe on foggy days.

10. Why does the narrator cut the last puzzle piece in half?

He does that so his dad and Charlie's dad can help finish it, like the bridge.

Pop's Bridge (continued)

Read the question below. Write complete sentences for your answer. Support your answer with information from the selection.

Linking to the Concepts Why was the Golden Gate Bridge important?

_____

_____

_____

_____

_____

Read the question below. Your answer should be based on your own experience. Write complete sentences for your answer.

Personal Response Write about a person who has done something that made you proud. Who is this person, and what did he or she do to make you proud?

_____

_____

_____

_____

_____

Pop's Bridge (continued)

Grammar, Usage, and Mechanics

Fill in the bubble beside the answer that is correct.

1. Which sentence has correct punctuation?
   - Ⓐ "My bike will be in the shop until Monday," Andy said.
   - Ⓑ "My bike will be in the shop" until Monday, Andy said.
   - Ⓒ My bike will be in the shop until Monday, Andy said.
   - Ⓓ none of the above

2. In which sentence are the verbs correct?
   - Ⓐ I woke up, and I has breakfast.
   - Ⓑ I woke up, and I had breakfast.
   - Ⓒ I will wake up, and I have breakfast.
   - Ⓓ none of the above

3. Which sentence has correct capitalization?
   - Ⓐ Andy asked, "would he let me use it this Weekend?"
   - Ⓑ Andy asked, "would he let me use it this weekend?"
   - Ⓒ Andy asked, "Would he let me use it this weekend?"
   - Ⓓ none of the above

4. Which sentence has correct capitalization and punctuation?
   - Ⓐ Bob answered "Maybe I should go ask him."
   - Ⓑ Andy said, "can I go with you to find out?"
   - Ⓒ That's a good idea, "Bob added."
   - Ⓓ none of the above

5. Which sentence has correct capitalization and punctuation?
   - Ⓐ Friends (Jim, Sharon, and others) saw him off.
   - Ⓑ "I think I am going to be late for school", Mia mumbled.
   - Ⓒ Yesterday Mom said, "put all your clothes away."
   - Ⓓ none of the above

Pop's Bridge (continued)

Analyzing the Selection

Read the question below. Write complete sentences for your answer. Support your answer with information from the selections.

How are the Golden Gate Bridge and the completion of the transcontinental railroad alike? Write about the people involved, the technology they used, and what was accomplished.

_____

_____

_____

_____

_____

_____

_____

_____

_____

_____

_____

_____

_____

_____

Pop's Bridge (continued)

Oral Fluency Assessment

Going to Alaska

"I would really love to go to Alaska," said Ben.	1–10
"Why?" asked Sue. "Isn't it cold and barren?"	11–18
"Not at all," he answered. "It is beautiful. The northern parts	19–29
are very cold most of the year, but Alaska is so large that the	30–43
southern part is very different."	44–48
The two went off to the library. There they found out more	49–60
about the state. It is nearly at the top of the world! They learned	61–74
that Alaska is the largest state. It is about one-fifth of the size	75–88
of all the rest of the states combined.	89–96
People who visit Alaska love its beauty. It has mountains,	97–106
valleys, lakes, and rivers. The highest mountain in North	107–115
America is in Alaska. The state has thousands of glaciers.	116–125
Many of Alaska's people are young. Most people who live	126–135
there have moved there from other states. The original people	136–145
of Alaska, the natives, are the Aleuts, the Eskimos, and three	146–156
groups of Native Americans.	157–160
"Okay, you win," said Sue. "Alaska would be a wonderful	161–170
place to visit, but I don't want to go there in the winter!"	171–183

EVALUATING CODES FOR ORAL FLUENCY

sky   (/) words read incorrectly

blue
 ^   sky   (^) inserted word
           ( ]) after the last word

READING RATE AND ACCURACY

Total Words Read: _____

Number of Errors: _____

Number of Correct Words
Read Per Minute (WPM):   _____

Accuracy Rate: _____

(Number of Correct Words Read per Minute ÷ Total Words Read)

READING FLUENCY

	Low	Average	High
Decoding ability	O	O	O
Pace	O	O	O
Syntax	O	O	O
Self-correction	O	O	O
Intonation	O	O	O

Record student rates on the Oral Fluency Scores pages.

Name _____ Date _____ Score _____

Narrative Writing

Writing Situation

What it would have been like to experience an event in American history

Audience

Students your age

Directions for Writing

You have read about some of the important events in American history. Imagine that you were at one of these events. Write a story about what happened from your point of view.

Checklist

You will score the most points if you

- choose an event in history you think is interesting.
- think about your ideas and plan your writing before you begin.
- put yourself in the story and think as if you were at the event.
- have a good beginning, middle, and end to your story.
- use sensory words so the reader can experience the event.
- tell about the characters in your story.
- make yourself one of the characters.
- tell about the place where the story happens.
- tell events in the order they happen.
- read your writing after you finish and check for mistakes.

Four Point Rubrics for Narrative Writing

	1 Point	2 Points	3 Points	4 Points
Genre				
Narrative	Narrative has missing details or elements. Logical order and narrative structure is unclear. Plot does not include a viable problem. Character development is not apparent. Setting does not include descriptions of where and when the narrative is set.	Narrative includes plot outline and some descriptive details and elements that add excitement or color, but narrative structure is not entirely clear. Character development is minimal. Setting includes minimal descriptions of where and when the narrative is set.	Narrative includes fairly well developed plot with descriptive details and other elements such as subplots that are integrated into the resolution. Narrative structure is clear. Characters are developed, though some characters may seem superficial. Setting includes descriptions of where and when the narrative is set.	Narrative includes more complicated plot lines with varied timelines, flashbacks, or dual story lines. Narrative structure is well defined. Characters well defined throughout, with unique qualities integral to the plot. Setting includes detailed descriptions of where and when the narrative is set.
Narrative: Theme	No theme is apparent.	Superficial theme is included but not integrated.	A theme is expressed but not well developed.	The narrative fully develops a theme that expresses an underlying message beyond the narrative plot.
Writing Traits				
Audience	Displays little or no sense of audience. Does not engage audience.	Displays some sense of audience.	Writes with audience in mind throughout.	Displays a strong sense of audience. Engages audience.
Voice	The writing provides little sense of involvement or commitment. There is no evidence that the writer has chosen a suitable voice.	The writer's commitment to the topic seems inconsistent. A sense of the writer may emerge at times; however, the voice is either inappropriately personal or inappropriately impersonal.	A voice is present. The writer demonstrates commitment to the topic. In places, the writing is expressive, engaging, or sincere. Words and expressions are clear and precise.	The writer has chosen a voice appropriate for the topic, purpose, and audience. Unique style comes through. The writing is expressive, engaging, or sincere. Strong commitment to the topic.
Writing Conventions				
Conventions Overall	Numerous errors in usage, grammar, spelling, capitalization, and punctuation repeatedly distract the reader and make the text difficult to read. The reader finds it difficult to focus on the message.	The writing demonstrates limited control of standard writing conventions (punctuation, spelling, capitalization, grammar, and usage). Errors sometimes impede readability.	The writing demonstrates control of standard writing conventions (punctuation, spelling, capitalization, grammar, and usage). Minor errors, while perhaps noticeable, do not impede readability.	The writing demonstrates exceptionally strong control of standard writing conventions (punctuation, spelling, capitalization, grammar, and usage) and uses them effectively to enhance communication. Errors are so few and so minor that the reader can easily skim over them.

Name _____ Date _____ Score _____

Erandi's Braids

Vocabulary

Read each item. Fill in the bubble for the answer you think is correct.

1. **Tremble** means about the same as

    Ⓐ worry.   Ⓒ shake.

    Ⓑ paint.   Ⓓ drink.

2. Which homophone pair best completes the sentence?

    The king was _____ off the _____ by the angry mob.

    Ⓐ led/lead   Ⓒ fined/find

    Ⓑ thrown/throne   Ⓓ sent/cent

3. The colors of **dawn** spread across the village of Patzcuaro. In this sentence, **dawn** means

    Ⓐ a very special party.   Ⓒ a picture being painted.

    Ⓑ ink.   Ⓓ the sun coming up.

4. Erandi gripped Mamá's hand and **huddled** in her skirt. **Huddled** means

    Ⓐ put on quickly.   Ⓒ went out to play

    Ⓑ wrapped tightly.   Ⓓ moved over.

5. Mamá's face reddened with **embarrassment. Embarrassment** is something like

    Ⓐ shame.   Ⓒ makeup.

    Ⓑ surprise.   Ⓓ happiness.

Erandi's Braids (continued)

Comprehension

Read the following questions carefully. Then completely fill in the bubble of each correct answer. You may look back at the selection to find the answer to each of the questions.

1. What does Mamá do right after she braids Erandi's hair?

- Ⓐ sells fish
- Ⓑ buys a dress for Erandi
- Ⓒ takes a nap
- Ⓓ makes tortillas

2. What does Erandi want for her birthday?

- Ⓐ a dress
- Ⓑ a fishing net
- Ⓒ a party
- Ⓓ money

Erandi's Braids (continued)

3. The hair will be used for all of these things EXCEPT

Ⓐ wigs.

Ⓑ eyelashes.

Ⓒ guitar strings.

Ⓓ fine embroidery.

4. Why is Mamá embarrassed?

Ⓐ The hair buyers do not want her hair.

Ⓑ She is unable to pay for Erandi's dress.

Ⓒ Erandi is making a lot of noise in the shop.

Ⓓ They have no money for the doll.

5. The author wrote this selection in order to

Ⓐ explain what life is like in Mexico.

Ⓑ teach how to catch fish.

Ⓒ show different uses for hair.

Ⓓ tell a story about making difficult choices.

Erandi's Braids (continued)

Read the following questions carefully. Use complete sentences to answer the questions. Possible answers below

6. Why are Erandi and her mother going to the lake?

Erandi and her mother are going to earn their living by catching fish.

7. What is the difference between Erandi's hair and her mother's?

Erandi's hair is longer and thicker than her mother's hair.

8. What choice does Erandi have to make in Señora Andrea's shop?

She has to choose between a doll and a dress as a birthday present.

9. Why do Erandi's knees tremble when she and her mother get to the front of the line at the barber shop?

Erandi is worried that her mother is planning to sell Erandi's braids.

10. Why are Erandi and her mother able to buy both a fishing net and the doll?

They get more money for Erandi's hair than expected.

Erandi's Braids (continued)

Read the question below. Write complete sentences for your answer. Support your answer with information from the selection.

Linking to the Concepts Is Erandi's mother proud of her? Give examples from the selection to support your answer.

_____

_____

_____

_____

_____

Read the question below. Your answer should be based on your own experience. Write complete sentences for your answer.

Personal Response What difficult choice have you had to make? Explain what the choice was and what you did.

_____

_____

_____

_____

Erandi's Braids (continued)

Grammar, Usage, and Mechanics

Read each question. Fill in the bubble beside the answer in each group that is correct. If none of the answers is correct, choose the last answer, "none of the above."

1. In which sentence is the underlined word used correctly?

Ⓐ It is <u>for</u> o'clock.   Ⓒ The <u>bear</u> roared.

Ⓑ My <u>ant</u> is here.   Ⓓ none of the above

2. In which sentence is the underlined word used correctly?

Ⓐ The sandwiches belong <u>here</u> on the table.

Ⓑ Sandy <u>maid</u> two dozen cupcakes for the picnic.

Ⓒ Grandmother handed Pat a <u>peace</u> of watermelon.

Ⓓ none of the above

3. In which sentence is the underlined word used correctly?

Ⓐ The officers have <u>scene</u> the robber trying to escape.

Ⓑ Please <u>wait</u> for Arnie at the corner.

Ⓒ Byron wanted a <u>read</u> bicycle.

Ⓓ none of the above

4. In which sentence is the underlined word used incorrectly?

Ⓐ Ling and Tia <u>ate</u> the apples that they picked.

Ⓑ Grandma <u>nose</u> three different languages.

Ⓒ An alpaca is often raised for <u>its</u> fur.

Ⓓ none of the above

5. Which sentence contains an appositive?

Ⓐ My teacher, Ms. Grant, is retiring.

Ⓑ The bright blue bird is new.

Ⓒ I heard a low, hollow rumble.

Ⓓ none of the above

Erandi's Braids (continued)

Analyzing the Selection

Read the questions below. Write complete sentences for your response. Support your answer with information from the selection.

Both Erandi and her mother did not want to sell Erandi's hair. Yet, they did it. Why were they both willing to make such a great sacrifice, despite how sad it made them? Do you think that what they gained was worth selling Erandi's hair?

_____

_____

_____

_____

_____

_____

_____

_____

_____

_____

_____

Erandi's Braids (continued)

Oral Fluency Assessment

April Fool's Traditions

Many people play jokes on their friends and families
on April Fool's Day. No one knows for sure where the idea of
playing tricks on other people started. Still, many people enjoy
this day.

Some think it began in 1564. A king changed to a new
calendar. On the old one, the year began on April 1. On the new
one, New Year's Day was January 1. Back then there was no
radio, newspaper, or television. Some people did not hear about
the change. So they celebrated on the wrong day. They were
"April fools."

In France, April first is called *April Fish*. Young fish do not
know they should stay away from hooks. They are easy to fool.
People who are easily tricked are called "April Fish." On April 1,
the children put pictures of fish on people's backs. When their
friends find the picture, they laugh and say, "April Fish!"

If you decide to play an April Fool's joke on a friend, be sure
it is funny. Think about the joke carefully so no one gets hurt.

1–9
10–22
23–32
33–34
35–46
47–60
61–72
73–82
83–93
94–95
96–107
108–119
120–131
132–142
143–152
153–166
167–179

**EVALUATING CODES
FOR ORAL FLUENCY**

sky   (/) words read incorrectly

blue
   ^   sky   (^) inserted word
            ( ]) after the last word

READING RATE AND ACCURACY

Total Words Read: _____

Number of Errors: _____

Number of Correct Words
Read Per Minute (WPM):   _____

Accuracy Rate: _____

(Number of Correct Words Read per
Minute ÷ Total Words Read)

READING FLUENCY

	Low	Average	High
Decoding ability	○	○	○
Pace	○	○	○
Syntax	○	○	○
Self-correction	○	○	○
Intonation	○	○	○

Record student rates on the Oral Fluency Scores pages.

Name _____ Date _____ Score _____

My Rows and Piles of Coins

Vocabulary

Read each item. Fill in the bubble for the answer you think is correct.

1. If something is **clutched,** it is

   (A) loosely wrapped. (C) lightly thrown.

   (B) emptied completely. (D) held tightly.

2. Which word best completes both sentences?

   Please read me the _____ again.

   We would like to add another _____ to the office building.

   (A) level (C) book

   (B) room (D) story

3. Saruni **longed** for a bicycle. **Longed** for means about the same as

   (A) learned to ride. (C) needed.

   (B) wanted very much. (D) sat on.

4. The family **pruned** coffee trees. They

   (A) cut the trees down.

   (B) trimmed the branches.

   (C) climbed the trees.

   (D) harvested coffee from the trees.

5. Murete **perched** on an orange motorbike. **Perched** means about the same as

   (A) sat. (C) tripped.

   (B) worked. (D) raced.

My Rows and Piles of Coins (continued)

Comprehension

Read the following questions carefully. Then completely fill in the bubble of each correct answer. You may look back at the selection to find the answer to each of the questions.

1. Which of these things does Saruni want to buy the most?

Ⓐ a toy truck

Ⓑ roasted peanuts

Ⓒ a bicycle

Ⓓ a kite

2. Why did the other children laugh?

Ⓐ Saruni is a wonderful storyteller.

Ⓑ Saruni is not very good at riding his father's bicycle.

Ⓒ They are playing a silly game with Saruni.

Ⓓ Saruni is doing tricks on his father's bicycle.

My Rows and Piles of Coins (continued)

3. Why do people not go to the market in March?

Ⓐ They buy enough supplies for two months in February.

Ⓑ They do not have anything to sell in March.

Ⓒ The market moves to another city.

Ⓓ The ground is too muddy.

4. At the end of the selection, it is clear that Saruni

Ⓐ will keep helping his family.

Ⓑ will buy a toy truck during his next trip to the market.

Ⓒ will stop working since he now has his bicycle.

Ⓓ will go to the market in March.

5. This selection is written from the first-person point of view of

Ⓐ a man with a new motorbike.

Ⓑ a man who sells bicycles.

Ⓒ a woman who works hard to support her family.

Ⓓ a young boy who wants a bicycle.

My Rows and Piles of Coins (continued)

Read the following questions carefully. Use complete sentences to answer the questions. Possible answers below

6. Why does Saruni's money box get heavier and heavier?

His mother gives him money every week, and he keeps saving it.

7. What sorts of things does Saruni's family sell at the market?

They sell beans, bananas, pumpkins, spinach, maize, firewood, and eggs.

8. Why does Saruni wear a jacket in July?

He lives south of the Equator, where it is cold during our summer months.

9. Why does the man selling bikes laugh at Saruni?

He laughs because the bicycles cost a lot more money than Saruni has.

10. What happens after Murete arrives home on a motorbike?

He sells his bike to Saruni, and Saruni gets the money back from Yeyo.

My Rows and Piles of Coins (continued)

Read the question below. Write complete sentences for your answer. Support your answer with information from the selection.

Linking to the Concepts What types of things does Saruni do to help his family?

_____

_____

_____

_____

_____

Read the question below. Your answer should be based on your own experience. Write complete sentences for your answer.

Personal Response Does saving money to buy something make you appreciate it more when you get it? Explain your answer.

_____

_____

_____

_____

_____

My Rows and Piles of Coins (continued)

Grammar, Usage, and Mechanics

Read each question. Fill in the bubble beside the answer in each group that is correct. If none of the answers is correct, choose the last answer, "none of the above."

1. Which sentence is correct?

Ⓐ There aren't no pears. Ⓒ There aren't any pears.

Ⓑ There aren't none pears. Ⓓ none of the above

2. Which sentence is correct?

Ⓐ Mom doesn't have any more carrot cake.

Ⓑ Mom doesn't have no more caret cake.

Ⓒ Mom doesn't have none more carat cake.

Ⓓ none of the above

3. Which sentence is correct?

Ⓐ This house doesn't have no flowers in the yard.

Ⓑ This house doesn't have any flowers in the yard.

Ⓒ This house doesn't have not one flower in the yard.

Ⓓ none of the above

4. Which sentence has a mistake?

Ⓐ Jay doesn't like any of the new television shows.

Ⓑ Kira can't find any of the pens she likes.

Ⓒ Lara isn't going to any soccer games this year.

Ⓓ none of the above

5. In which sentence is the underlined word used incorrectly?

Ⓐ I need to have my car <u>towed</u>.

Ⓑ Which <u>won</u> of these do you like best?

Ⓒ Paola had a <u>pair</u> of pink socks with cats on them.

Ⓓ none of the above

My Rows and Piles of Coins (continued)

Analyzing the Selection

Read the question below. Write complete sentences for your answer. Support your answer with information from the selection.

Do you think Saruni uses his money wisely? Explain your answer.

_____

_____

_____

_____

_____

_____

_____

_____

_____

_____

_____

_____

My Rows and Piles of Coins (continued)

Oral Fluency Assessment

The Computer Age

Computers are everywhere. They are in schools, offices, and
homes. People carry small computers with them. They often use
them on trains or in parks.

People of all ages use computers. Young children learn
and play on them. Older people stay in touch with friends and
family. They have become part of our lives because they are
cheaper than ever.

Today's computers are small enough to fit in your hand. This
was not always true. Years ago, computers were as big as a
room. They had to be kept in special places. These places had to
be clean and cool.

People use computers to do many things. They write papers,
print photos, and send e-mail. They study space and explore
the oceans on the Internet. Doctors even use computers to look
inside the body.

Some computers are no bigger than a dime. These types
are found in things like cars and cameras. They make these
machines work. People sometimes call these machines "smart,"
but they are not. The people who make the machines are the
smart ones!

1–9
10–19
20–25
26–34
35–46
47–57
58–60
61–71
72–83
84–96
97–100
101–110
111–120
121–131
132–134
135–144
145–155
156–163
164–175
176–179

EVALUATING CODES FOR ORAL FLUENCY

sky   (/) words read incorrectly

blue
^   sky   (^) inserted word
           ( ]) after the last word

READING RATE AND ACCURACY

Total Words Read: _____

Number of Errors: _____

Number of Correct Words
Read Per Minute (WPM):   _____

Accuracy Rate: _____

(Number of Correct Words Read per
Minute ÷ Total Words Read)

READING FLUENCY

	Low	Average	High
Decoding ability	○	○	○
Pace	○	○	○
Syntax	○	○	○
Self-correction	○	○	○
Intonation	○	○	○

Record student rates on the Oral Fluency Scores pages.

Name _____ **Date** _____ **Score** _____

A Spoon for Every Bite

Vocabulary

Read each item. Fill in the bubble for the answer you think is correct.

1. Each of these examples is a superlative form EXCEPT

Ⓐ slowest.

Ⓒ tastiest.

Ⓑ most thoughtful.

Ⓓ guiltier.

2. Another word for **fine** is

Ⓐ very sleepy.

Ⓒ very fast.

Ⓑ very helpful.

Ⓓ very nice.

3. The couple's neighbor was proud of his **wealth.** This means he was proud of his

Ⓐ children.

Ⓑ money.

Ⓒ car.

Ⓓ clothes.

4. The servant **demanded** to know what the couple had given his master. **Demanded** means

Ⓐ joked.

Ⓑ dared.

Ⓒ asked firmly.

Ⓓ feared.

5. The couple's neighbor had many **possessions.** **Possessions** are

Ⓐ challenges in life.

Ⓒ servants.

Ⓑ things.

Ⓓ fields of crops.

A Spoon for Every Bite (continued)

Comprehension

Read the following questions carefully. Then completely fill in the bubble of each correct answer. You may look back at the selection to find the answer to each of the questions.

1. What does the couple have two of at the beginning of the selection?

   Ⓐ coins

   Ⓑ cars

   Ⓒ babies

   Ⓓ spoons

2. After having dinner with the poor couple, why does the rich man stay awake that night?

   Ⓐ Something he ate has kept him awake.

   Ⓑ He was thinking about what the couple had said.

   Ⓒ There were dogs howling outside his window.

   Ⓓ The couple had served him too much food.

A Spoon for Every Bite (continued)

3. Why does the neighbor's servant go to the poor couple's house?

Ⓐ His master is acting oddly, and the servant thinks they know why.

Ⓑ His master had left his coat at the couple's house the night before.

Ⓒ The servant needs to borrow a spoon from the couple.

Ⓓ The servant wants to give the couple vegetables from the garden.

4. After a year, why does the neighbor return to the couple's house?

Ⓐ There is a party for the baby's first birthday.

Ⓑ He wants to know how anyone can have a spoon for every bite.

Ⓒ He has been trying to make the soup and wants the woman's recipe.

Ⓓ He wants some of his spoons back.

5. Why does the couple's friend not reuse his spoon?

Ⓐ It has to be washed before it can be used again.

Ⓑ It bent when he used it.

Ⓒ It is eaten after every bite.

Ⓓ It gets dropped on the floor.

A Spoon for Every Bite (continued)

Read the following questions carefully. Use complete sentences to answer the questions. Possible answers below

6. How is the poor couple different from their neighbor at the beginning of the selection?

He is rich with a big house and many things. They only have two spoons.

7. Why does the poor couple not invite the neighbor to dinner on the night of the baptism?

They waited until they bought another spoon before inviting the neighbor.

8. How does the rich man become poor?

The rich man sells all he owns to get money to buy spoons for every bite.

9. How is a piece of tortilla like a spoon?

A piece of tortilla is like a spoon because it can be used to scoop food.

10. How is the couple going to live in comfort for the rest of their lives?

They will get money by selling the spoons the rich man threw away.

A Spoon for Every Bite (continued)

Read the question below. Write complete sentences for your answer. Support your answer with information from the selection.

Linking to the Concepts What makes the couple's neighbor a foolish man?

_____

_____

_____

_____

_____

Read the question below. Your answer should be based on your own experience. Write complete sentences for your answer.

Personal Response Write about something you think people do that is wasteful. Why do you think it is wasteful?

_____

_____

_____

_____

_____

_____

A Spoon for Every Bite (continued)

Grammar, Usage, and Mechanics

In questions 1–4, fill in the bubble beside the answer in each group that is the best way to combine the sentences with a participial phrase.

1. **The bird ate some berries. The berries were on a bush.**
   - Ⓐ The bird on a bush ate some berries.
   - Ⓑ The bird ate some berries on a bush.
   - Ⓒ The bird ate on a bush some berries.
   - Ⓓ none of the above

2. **Gene watched Jim. Jim was diving into the water.**
   - Ⓐ Gene diving into the water watched the Jim.
   - Ⓑ Gene watched Jim diving into the water.
   - Ⓒ Gene watched the water diving into Jim.
   - Ⓓ none of the above

3. **Lena laughed at the dog. The dog was chasing its tail.**
   - Ⓐ Chasing its tail, Lena laughed at the dog.
   - Ⓑ Lena, chasing a dog, laughed at the dog.
   - Ⓒ Lena laughed at the dog chasing its tail.
   - Ⓓ none of the above

4. **He roped the horse. The horse was racing in the field.**
   - Ⓐ He roped the horse racing in the field.
   - Ⓑ He racing in the field roped the horse.
   - Ⓒ He roped racing the horse in the field.
   - Ⓓ none of the above

5. Which of these is an example of a double negative?
   - Ⓐ Didn't I get any?
   - Ⓒ Why did I get none?
   - Ⓑ I can't go anywhere.
   - Ⓓ Didn't you get none?

A Spoon for Every Bite (continued)

Analyzing the Selection

Read the questions below. Write complete sentences for your answer. Support your answer with information from the selections.

How is the rich man in this selection different from Erandi, Saruni, and their families? How is the poor couple similar to Erandi, Saruni, and their families?

_____

_____

_____

_____

_____

_____

_____

_____

_____

_____

A Spoon for Every Bite (continued)

Oral Fluency Assessment

Hale-Bopp!

Look! Up in the sky! It's a bird! It's a plane! It's a . . . comet?	1–14
A comet is really just a large frozen ball of dirt and dust. It	15–28
flies through space at over forty-three thousand miles per hour.	29–39
As it warms, its material turns to vapor. A giant cloud of gas	40–52
surrounds the comet. The silvery tail is the vapor it makes. The	53–64
tail can stretch out for millions of miles.	65–72
Hale-Bopp is a large comet that showed up in our sky not	73–85
so long ago. Everybody who saw the comet had an experience	86–96
they will not forget soon. They saw something really unique.	97–106
Why? Well, Comet Hale-Bopp will not be seen here on Earth	107–118
again for two thousand years.	119–123
Comets are named for the people who first see them. Alan	124–134
Hale and Tom Bopp first saw their comet in July of 1995. That is	135–148
how this comet got its name.	149–154
The comet Hale and Bopp gave their names to did not let us	155–167
down. But some other comets have. Halley's Comet visits Earth	168–177
every sixty-four years. On its last visit, it was not very bright.	178–190

EVALUATING CODES FOR ORAL FLUENCY

sky   (/) words read incorrectly

blue
   ^   sky   (^) inserted word
            ( ]) after the last word

READING RATE AND ACCURACY

Total Words Read: _____

Number of Errors: _____

Number of Correct Words
Read Per Minute (WPM):   _____

Accuracy Rate: _____

(Number of Correct Words Read per
Minute ÷ Total Words Read)

READING FLUENCY

	Low	Average	High
Decoding ability	O	O	O
Pace	O	O	O
Syntax	O	O	O
Self-correction	O	O	O
Intonation	O	O	O

Record student rates on the Oral Fluency Scores pages.

Name _____ Date _____ Score _____

Three Fables

Vocabulary

Read each item. Fill in the bubble for the answer you think is correct.

1. What is the correct contraction of *do not?*

Ⓐ do'not   Ⓒ dont

Ⓑ don't   Ⓓ do'nt

2. Misfortune means about the same as

Ⓐ bad luck.   Ⓒ travels.

Ⓑ event.   Ⓓ hard work.

3. The farmer's daughter began to **daydream** as she walked. When you **daydream,** you

Ⓐ let your mind wander.

Ⓑ hop and skip with joy.

Ⓒ look around carefully.

Ⓓ push a heavy object.

4. The milk will **provide** the farmer's daughter with cream. **Provide** means about the same as

Ⓐ mix.

Ⓑ trick.

Ⓒ fill

Ⓓ give.

5. The **miser** sold everything he had. A **miser** is someone who

Ⓐ is a very good actor.   Ⓒ loves money.

Ⓑ farms the land.   Ⓓ takes care of sheep.

Three Fables (continued)

Comprehension

Read the following questions carefully. Then completely fill in the bubble of each correct answer. You may look back at the selection to find the answer to each of the questions.

1. What happens when the milkmaid tosses her head?

Ⓐ The chickens begin to hatch.

Ⓑ The young men ask her to dance.

Ⓒ The milk spills from the pail.

Ⓓ The milk turns into butter.

2. What causes the miser to scream in fury?

Ⓐ He cannot lift his gold.

Ⓑ He discovers his gold is stolen.

Ⓒ His brick is not in its hiding place.

Ⓓ His neighbor refuses to tell him where the gold is.

Three Fables (continued)

3. Why is the rooster scratching the ground?

    Ⓐ He is hungry and is looking for food.

    Ⓑ He knows a lady has lost her jewel.

    Ⓒ He is digging for gold.

    Ⓓ He is burying the jewel to hide it from its owner.

4. How are the rooster and the miser alike?

    Ⓐ Both are hungry.

    Ⓑ Both like jewels.

    Ⓒ Both have things they cannot use.

    Ⓓ Both have their gold buried in a field.

5. Aesop wrote these fables

    Ⓐ to show how roosters are not very smart.

    Ⓑ to explain why gold is not important.

    Ⓒ to tell how to start a business.

    Ⓓ to teach important lessons.

Three Fables (continued)

Read the following questions carefully. Use complete sentences to answer the questions. Possible answers below

6. How is the milkmaid going to get eggs from the milk?

She is going to sell the cream from the milk to buy the eggs.

7. How does the milkmaid think people will react to her at the dance?

She thinks all the young fellows will admire her and ask her to dance.

8. What happens right after the miser's workman follows the miser?

He finds where the miser has buried the lump of gold and steals it.

9. Why does the rooster not care about the jewel?

It is hungry, and it would rather have a kernel of corn than a jewel.

10. How is a brick like the miser's gold?

The miser did nothing with his gold, so it is worthless as a brick.

Three Fables (continued)

Read the question below. Write complete sentences for your answer. Support your answer with information from the selection.

Linking to the Concepts What lesson do these fables teach about value?

_____

_____

_____

_____

Read the question below. Your answer should be based on your own experience. Write complete sentences for your answer.

Personal Response Have you ever made grand plans that did not come true? Explain what happened and what you learned.

_____

_____

_____

_____

_____

Three Fables (continued)

Grammar, Usage, and Mechanics

Read each question. Fill in the bubble beside the answer in each group that is correct. If none of the answers is correct, choose the last answer, "none of the above."

1. Which pronoun can take the place of the underlined part?

Mom wanted <u>Dyan and me</u> to clean the kitchen.

Ⓐ us   Ⓒ them

Ⓑ we   Ⓓ none of the above

2. Which pronoun can take the place of the underlined part?

<u>Peggy and Tyrone</u> fed the stray dog.

Ⓐ We   Ⓒ Them

Ⓑ They   Ⓓ none of the above

3. Which sentence is correct?

Ⓐ That new movie doesnt' for two hours start.

Ⓑ That for two hours movie does'nt start new.

Ⓒ That new movie doesn't start for two hours.

Ⓓ none of the above

4. Which sentence has a misplaced modifier?

Ⓐ The man read a book in a gray suit.

Ⓑ There was a tear in the shirt Bill had bought.

Ⓒ They ran over the hurdles.

Ⓓ none of the above

5. Which sentence has correct punctuation?

Ⓐ She saw eagles' nests.   Ⓒ She saw eagles's nests.

Ⓑ She saw eagles nests.   Ⓓ none of the above

Three Fables (continued)

Analyzing the Selection

Read the question below. Write complete sentences for your answer. Support your answer with information from the selection.

Do you think people understand Aesop's fables better now than they did long ago? Explain your answer.

_____

_____

_____

_____

_____

_____

_____

_____

_____

_____

_____

_____

Three Fables (continued)

Oral Fluency Assessment

The Summer Cookout

In almost every home, summer holidays usually mean a	1–9
cookout. The smell of cooking food on a warm day can be one	10–22
of the best memories of summer. It is one of the best smells to	23–36
say the least!	37–39
The most common cookout foods are the hot dog and	40–49
hamburger. Steaks are more of a special treat. Chicken and fish	50–60
can also be cooked on the grill.	61–67
Many people are surprised to learn that vegetables can	68–76
be cooked on a grill. Potatoes have a great new flavor when	77–88
cooked on a grill. So do corn, peppers, and onions. Tomatoes,	89–99
mushrooms, and squash can be grilled. They take a bit more	100–110
work and care. These soft foods can be easily overcooked.	111–120
They may also fall through the spaces in the grill.	121–130
There are a number of ways to grill. Many people like to	131–142
grill over charcoal. For added taste, they add chips from oak	143–153
or other trees to the mix. Some grills burn a gas. Gas grills are	154–167
popular because they are so simple to use. They also heat up	168–179
quickly.	180

**EVALUATING CODES
FOR ORAL FLUENCY**

sky   (/) words read incorrectly

blue
^   sky   (^) inserted word
              ( ]) after the last word

READING RATE AND ACCURACY

Total Words Read: _____

Number of Errors: _____

Number of Correct Words
Read Per Minute (WPM):   _____

Accuracy Rate: _____

(Number of Correct Words Read per
Minute ÷ Total Words Read)

READING FLUENCY

	Low	Average	High
Decoding ability	O	O	O
Pace	O	O	O
Syntax	O	O	O
Self-correction	O	O	O
Intonation	O	O	O

Record student rates on the Oral Fluency Scores pages.

Name _____ Date _____ Score _____

Business Is Looking Up

Vocabulary

Read each item. Fill in the bubble for the answer you think is correct.

1. What is the comparative form of the adjective **corny?**

Ⓐ cornier

Ⓒ cornierest

Ⓑ corniest

Ⓓ most corny

2. A **century** is

Ⓐ twenty-four hours.

Ⓒ one thousand years.

Ⓑ ten years.

Ⓓ one hundred years.

3. Jinx thinks Renaldo will need a **partner** for his business. A **partner** is

Ⓐ someone who helps you move around.

Ⓑ something with which to cut paper.

Ⓒ someone who owns a business with you.

Ⓓ someone who tells you how to make money.

4. Renaldo started to count his **profits. Profits** are

Ⓐ money a business makes.

Ⓑ special greeting cards.

Ⓒ anything you count to make you fall asleep.

Ⓓ designs that can be copied.

5. A successful business needs a good **product. A product** is

Ⓐ someone to help you sell things.

Ⓑ an item sold by a business.

Ⓒ a customer.

Ⓓ a way to get from place to place.

Business Is Looking Up (continued)

Comprehension

Read the following questions carefully. Then completely fill in the bubble of each correct answer. You may look back at the selection to find the answer to each of the questions.

1. Who is narrating this selection?

Ⓐ a man who has been in business for a long time

Ⓑ a boy who wants to make money

Ⓒ a woman who owns a card shop

Ⓓ a girl who draws very well

2. Why does Renaldo think that people need his cards?

Ⓐ He knows that people like to give other people cards.

Ⓑ He knows that many people are part of stepfamilies.

Ⓒ He has tried to buy cards before and knows how difficult it is.

Ⓓ He thinks that most cards are not funny enough.

Business Is Looking Up (continued)

3. How are Renaldo and Jinx alike?

Ⓐ Both can think things through carefully.

Ⓑ Both are artistic.

Ⓒ Both have a lot of money.

Ⓓ Both are excited about the business.

4. What type of card does Jinx first read to Renaldo?

Ⓐ a card a mother gives to her daughter on her anniversary

Ⓑ a get well card

Ⓒ a stepcard that somebody else has already thought of

Ⓓ a card someone would give to a couple who has had a baby

5. Why does Mrs. Rothman need Renaldo's cards?

Ⓐ Her neighbor is sick in the hospital.

Ⓑ Her daughter is celebrating her anniversary.

Ⓒ Her son has married a woman with twins.

Ⓓ Her husband is out of town and she misses him.

Business Is Looking Up (continued)

Read the following questions carefully. Use complete sentences to answer the questions. Possible answers below

6. How is the Woodburn School and Community Center like a city?

There are people of all ages there, and there are lots of things to do.

7. Why are Renaldo and Jinx at the card shop?

They want to see if somebody else has thought of stepcards.

8. What do Jinx and Renaldo do after they finish thirty-four cards?

Jinx and Renaldo go to the Woodburn School and Community Center.

9. Why do Jinx and Renaldo go to Renaldo's mom?

Jinx and Renaldo needed advice from someone in the business world.

10. What is different about the way Jinx and Renaldo act after they sell their first batch of cards?

Renaldo wants to spend his money, but Jinx wants to reinvest the money.

UNIT 6 Lesson 5

Business Is Looking Up (continued)

Read the question below. Write complete sentences for your answer. Support your answer with information from the selection.

Linking to the Concepts What are some things you need to do before you start a business?

_____

_____

_____

_____

_____

Read the questions below. Your answer should be based on your own experience. Write complete sentences for your answer.

Personal Response What business would you like to start? Why?

_____

_____

_____

_____

_____

Business Is Looking Up (continued)

Grammar, Usage, and Mechanics

Read each question. Fill in the bubble beside the answer in each group that is correct. If none of the answers is correct, choose the last answer, "none of the above."

1. In which item is the adjective used correctly?

Ⓐ the curliest hair in class   Ⓒ the curlierest hair in class

Ⓑ the more curlier hair   Ⓓ none of the above
   in class

2. In which sentence is the adverb used correctly?

Ⓐ Pedro spoke clearest than Randy.

Ⓑ Pedro spoke more clearly than Randy.

Ⓒ Pedro spoke clearlier than Randy.

Ⓓ none of the above

3. Which of these is a simple sentence?

Ⓐ After we ate, we went to the circus.

Ⓑ We waited in line, and my sister paid her own way.

Ⓒ Once we sat down, she ordered a water.

Ⓓ none of the above

4. Which of these is a complex sentence?

Ⓐ Our teacher gave us a science assignment.

Ⓑ The project was difficult, but everybody did their part.

Ⓒ After the project was finished, we had a party.

Ⓓ none of the above

5. Which of these is a complex sentence?

Ⓐ Grandma wanted to make apple pies.

Ⓑ When we found the ladder, we climbed the tree.

Ⓒ We picked and sorted the apples.

Ⓓ none of the above

Business Is Looking Up (continued)

Analyzing the Selection

Read the questions below. Write complete sentences for your answer. Support your answer with information from the selections.

Jinx and Renaldo earn money by working. What other characters in this unit earned money? What does the unit teach you about the ways you can make money?

_____

_____

_____

_____

_____

_____

_____

_____

_____

_____

_____

_____

Business Is Looking Up (continued)

Oral Fluency Assessment

Playtime

Did you watch television yesterday or listen to the radio? 1–10
Maybe you played soccer with your friends. All of these are 11–21
normal pastimes today. However, over two hundred years 22–29
ago, during colonial times, children spent their free time much 30–39
differently. 40

For one thing, children living in colonial America did not 41–50
have much free time. They were expected to do chores. Girls 51–61
mostly worked inside the house. They sewed, cooked, and 62–70
cleaned. Boys helped take care of animals and worked on 71–80
the farm. 81–82

Many of these children did not go to school. However, their 83–93
chores took up most of their time. When they did have time, 94–105
they spent most of it playing outdoors. 106–112

You might know some of the games they played. They liked 113–123
to jump rope and play with marbles. They liked to swim, run 124–135
races, and play tag. 136–139

Chances are that you have never heard of quoits, stool-ball, 140–150
or rolling hoops. These might sound strange to you. However, 151–160
these were popular with colonial children. Think how strange 161–169
they would find some of your games. Would you be able to 170–181
explain the rules of football? Could you tell them what was 182–192
going on in a video game? 193–198

**EVALUATING CODES
FOR ORAL FLUENCY**

sky   (/) words read incorrectly

blue
^   sky   (^) inserted word
           ( ]) after the last word

READING RATE AND ACCURACY

Total Words Read: _____

Number of Errors: _____

Number of Correct Words
Read Per Minute (WPM):   _____

Accuracy Rate: _____

(Number of Correct Words Read per
Minute ÷ Total Words Read)

READING FLUENCY

	Low	Average	High
Decoding ability	O	O	O
Pace	O	O	O
Syntax	O	O	O
Self-correction	O	O	O
Intonation	O	O	O

Record student rates on the Oral Fluency Scores pages.

Name _____ **Date** _____ **Score** _____

Persuasive Writing

Writing Situation
Starting your own business

Audience
Someone who might give you money to start your business

Directions for Writing
Many people start their own businesses. Write about a business you would like to start. Tell about the business and why it would be successful. Explain why investing in this business is a good idea.

Checklist
You will earn the best score if you
- think about your ideas and plan your writing before you begin.
- write for a person who might give you money to start your business.
- describe your business idea clearly in the first paragraph.
- show that you care about the business.
- write in a way that is convincing to your readers.
- keep the focus of your writing on the business and why it will succeed.
- vary your sentences and the words you use.
- tell about the people who would use your business.
- use words that tell how you feel about the business.
- read your writing after you finish and check for mistakes.

Four Point Rubrics for Persuasive Writing

Genre	1 Point	2 Points	3 Points	4 Points
Persuasive	Position is absent or confusing. Insufficient writing to show that criteria are met.	Position is vague or lacks clarity. Unrelated ideas or multiple positions are included.	An opening statement identifies position. Writing may develop few or more points than delineated in opening. Focus may be too broad.	Sets scope and purpose of paper in introduction. Maintains position throughout. Supports arguments. Includes effective closing.
Writing Traits				
Audience	Displays little or no sense of audience. Does not engage audience.	Displays some sense of audience.	Writes with audience in mind throughout.	Displays a strong sense of audience. Engages audience.
Focus	Topic is unclear or wanders and must be inferred. Extraneous material may be present.	Topic/position/direction is unclear and must be inferred.	Topic/position is stated and direction/ purpose is previewed and maintained. Mainly stays on topic.	Topic/position is clearly stated, previewed, and maintained throughout the paper. Topics and details are tied together with a central theme or purpose that is maintained /threaded throughout the paper.
Organization	The writing lacks coherence; organization seems haphazard and disjointed. Plan is not evident. Facts are presented randomly. No transitions are included. Beginning is weak and ending is abrupt. There is no awareness of paragraph structure or organization.	An attempt has been made to organize the writing; however, the overall structure is inconsistent or skeletal. Plan is evident but loosely structured or writer overuses a particular pattern. Writing may be a listing of facts/ideas with a weak beginning or conclusion. Transitions are awkward or nonexistent. Includes beginning use of paragraphs.	Organization is clear and coherent. Order and structure are present, but may seem formulaic. Plan is evident. Reasons for order of key concepts may be unclear. Beginning or conclusion is included but may lack impact. Transitions are present. Paragraph use is appropriate.	The organization enhances the central idea and its development. The order and structure are compelling and move the reader through the text easily. Plan is evident. Key concepts are logically sequenced. Beginning grabs attention. Conclusion adds impact. Uses a variety of transitions that enhance meaning. Uses paragraphs appropriately.
Writing Conventions				
Conventions Overall	Numerous errors in usage, grammar, spelling, capitalization, and punctuation repeatedly distract the reader and make the text difficult to read. The reader finds it difficult to focus on the message.	The writing demonstrates limited control of standard writing conventions (punctuation, spelling, capitalization, grammar, and usage). Errors sometimes impede readability.	The writing demonstrates control of standard writing conventions (punctuation, spelling, capitalization, grammar, and usage). Minor errors, while perhaps noticeable, do not impede readability.	The writing demonstrates exceptionally strong control of standard writing conventions (punctuation, spelling, capitalization, grammar, and usage) and uses them effectively to enhance communication. Errors are so few and so minor that the reader can easily skim over them.

Six Point Rubrics

Use the following rubrics to assess student writing.

6 Points

The writing is focused, purposeful, and reflects insight into the writing situation. The paper conveys a sense of completeness and wholeness with adherence to the main idea, and its organizational pattern provides for a logical progression of ideas. The support is substantial, specific, relevant, concrete, and/or illustrative. The paper demonstrates a commitment to and an involvement with the subject, clarity in presentation of ideas, and may use creative writing strategies appropriate to the purpose of the paper. The writing demonstrates a mature command of language (word choice) with freshness of expression. Sentence structure is varied, and sentences are complete except when fragments are used purposefully. Few, if any, convention errors occur in mechanics, usage, and punctuation.

5 Points

The writing focuses on the topic, and its organizational pattern provides for a progression of ideas, although some lapses may occur. The paper conveys a sense of completeness or wholeness. The support is ample. The writing demonstrates a mature command of language, including precise word choice. There is variation in sentence structure, and, with rare exceptions, sentences are complete except when fragments are used purposefully. The paper generally follows the conventions of mechanics, usage, and spelling.

4 Points

The writing is generally focused on the topic but may include extraneous or loosely related material. An organizational pattern is apparent, although some lapses may occur. The paper exhibits some sense of completeness or wholeness. The support, including word choice, is adequate, although development may be uneven. There is little variation in sentence structure, and most sentences are complete. The paper generally follows the conventions of mechanics, usage, and spelling.

3 Points

The writing is generally focused on the topic but may include extraneous or loosely related material. An organizational pattern has been attempted, but the paper may lack a sense of completeness or wholeness. Some support is included, but developemt is erratic. Word choice is adequate but may be limited, predictable, or occasionally vague. There is little, if any, variation in sentence structure. Knowledge of the conventions of mechanics and usage is usually demonstrated, and commonly used words are usually spelled correctly.

2 Points

The writing is related to the topic but includes extraneous or loosely related material. Little evidence of an organizational pattern may be demonstrated, and the paper may lack a sense of completeness or wholeness. Development of support is inadequate or illogical. Word choice is limited, inappropriate, or vague. There is little, if any, variation in sentence structure, and gross errors in sentence structure may occur. Errors in basic conventions of mechanics and usage may occur, and commonly used words may be misspelled.

1 Point

The writing may only minimally address the topic. The paper is fragmentary or incoherent listing of related ideas or sentences or both. Little, if any, development of support or an organizational pattern or both is apparent. Limited or inappropriate word choice may obscure meaning. Gross errors in sentence structure and usage may impede communication. Frequent and blatant errors may occur in the basic conventions of mechanics and usage, and commonly used words may be misspelled.

Unscorable

The paper is unscorable because

- the response is not related to what the prompt requested the student to do.
- the response is simply a rewording of the prompt
- the response is a copy of a published work.
- the student refused to write.
- the response is illegible.

- the response is incomprehensible (words are arrange in such a way that no meaning is conveyed).
- the response contains an insufficient amount of writing to determine if the student was attempting to address the prompt.

Oral Fluency Scores

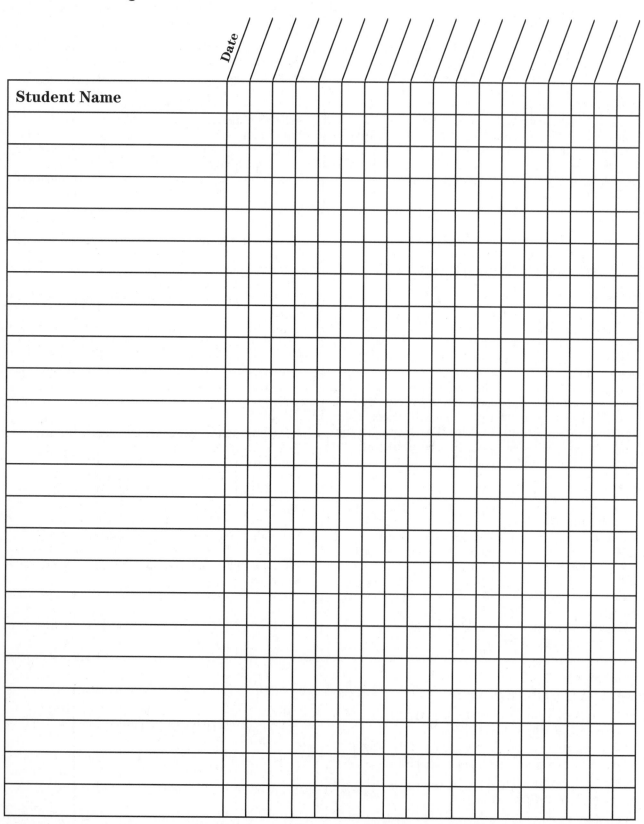

Student Name	Date															

Oral Fluency Scores

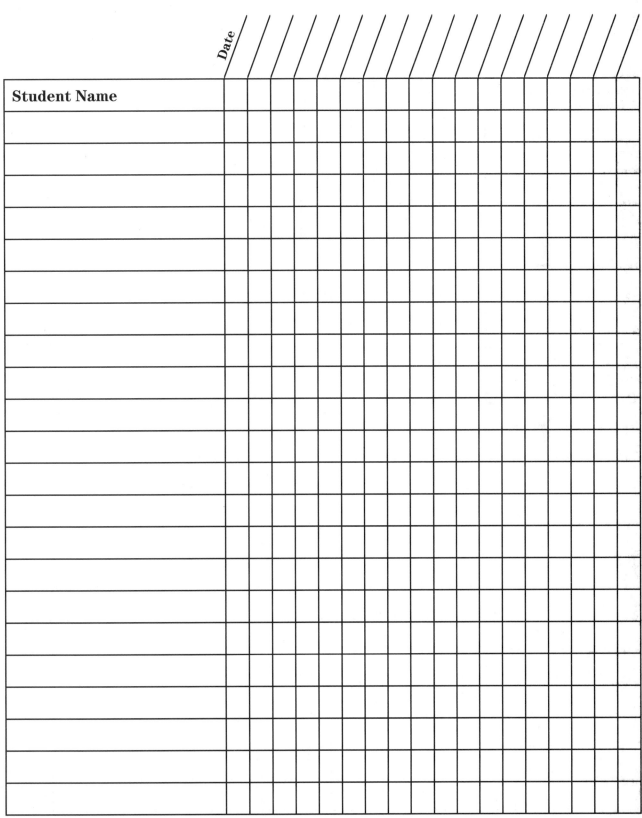

Student Name	Date															

Class Assessment Record

Student Name	Unit 4, Lesson 1	Unit 4, Lesson 2	Unit 4, Lesson 3	Unit 4, Lesson 4	Unit 4, Lesson 5	Unit 4 Writing Prompt	Unit 5, Lesson 1	Unit 5, Lesson 2	Unit 5, Lesson 3

Class Assessment Record

Student Name	Unit 5, Lesson 4	Unit 5, Lesson 5	Unit 5 Writing Prompt	Unit 6, Lesson 1	Unit 6, Lesson 2	Unit 6, Lesson 3	Unit 6, Lesson 4	Unit 6, Lesson 5	Unit 6 Writing Prompt

Student Assessment Record

Name_____

Teacher _____ **Grade** _____

Unit/ Lesson	Assessment Section	Date	Number Possible	Number Right	%	Score (Rubrics/WPM)

Comprehension Observation Log

Student _____ **Date** _____

Unit _____ **Lesson** _____ **Selection Title** _____

General Comprehension
Concepts discussed: _____
_____

Behavior Within a Group
Articulates, expresses ideas: _____
_____

Joins discussions: _____
_____

Collaborates (such as *works well with other students, works alone*): _____
_____

Role in Group
Role (such as *leader, summarizer, questioner, critic, observer, non-participant*): _____
_____

Flexibility (changes roles when necessary): _____
_____

Use of Reading Strategies
Uses strategies when needed (either those taught or student's choice of strategy)/Describes strategies used:
_____
_____
_____

Changes strategies when appropriate: _____
_____

Changes Since Last Observation
_____
_____
_____
